ISO 9001:2000
Internal Audits
Made Easy

ISO 9001:2000 Internal Audits Made Easy

Tools, Techniques and Step-By-Step
Guidelines for Successful
Internal Audits

ANN W. PHILLIPS

ISO 9001:2000 Internal Audits Made Easy

Inquiries should be addressed to:

Quality Techniques
P.O. Box 5007
Huntsville, AL 35814
aphillips@omnitechintl.com
256-883-3554

FIRST EDITION

Library of Congress Control Number 2002093408

ISBN 0-9722846-0-5

Printed in the United States of America
At Morgan Printing, Austin, Texas

Table of Contents

Acknowledgements 9

Preface 11

Chapter 1:   Introduction to Internal Auditing
            for ISO 9001:2000 15

- Purpose of the internal audit
- Objectives of the internal audit
- Benefits of an effective internal audit process

Chapter 2:   Creating an Environment
            for Successful Audits 25

- Gaining management's support for the audit process
- Gaining employees' support for the audit process
- After the audit

Chapter 3:   Selecting and Maintaining
            the Internal Audit Team 44

- Is your audit pool adequately staffed?
- What job functions should be represented
  in the audit pool?

- What personal attributes make good internal auditors?
- How can an organization maintain the audit pool?

Chapter 4: Typical Responsibilities and Authorities in the Audit Process 53

- Management representative / audit coordinator
- Auditee's management
- Auditors

Chapter 5: Audit Preparation 78

- Define and understand the scope of the audit
- Review the requirements of applicable standards
- Review applicable documentation
- Prepare a process model
- Review previous audit results
- Create an effective checklist
- Conduct a pre-audit meeting

Chapter 6: Performing the Audit 119

- The "group" opening meeting
- The "individual" opening meeting
- Interview techniques
- Basic communication skills
- Keys to listening
- Effective use of the checklist
- Sampling data
- Handling difficult auditees

Chapter 7: Reporting the Audit 149

- Types of audit findings
- Writing effective Corrective Action Requests
- The audit report
- The closing meeting

Chapter 8: Follow-Up Audit Activities 159

- Verifying the effectiveness of corrective actions

Appendix A: Sample Process Models 167
      (also provided on CD)

- Quality planning
- Management review
- Competence, awareness and training
- Maintenance
- Planning for product realization
- Customer-related processes
- Design and development control
- Purchasing
- Product or service realization
- Control of monitoring and measuring equipment
- Customer satisfaction
- Internal quality audit
- Monitoring and measurement of product
- Corrective action
- Preventive action

Appendix B: Sample Audit Checklist 185
    (also provided on CD)

Appendix C: Audit Preparation Example 249
    (also provided on CD)

- ACME training procedure
- ACME Job Description
- ACME Training Checklist
- Sample audit checklist for Acme's training process

Appendix D: Sample Audit Forms 261
    (also provided on CD)

- Audit Schedule Matrix
- Audit Summary Report
- Corrective Action Request (CAR)
- Corrective Action Request Log
- Audit Action Item List

Acknowledgements

I would sincerely like to thank those that supported me during the writing of this book and those that contributed so greatly to its content.

To Janeen Santarosa—thank you for the inspiration to put this book in writing.

To Fran Crumley, Leslie Rowell, Joanne Weik, Maria Williams, and Lori Darcy—thank you for your thoughtful reviews and insightful suggestions for making this book more practical and user-friendly.

To my dad, Gene Welborn—thank you for giving me the desire to write and for sharing with me your knowledge and experience in writing and publishing.

Most of all, to my wonderful husband, Eddie—thank you so much for your patience, your reviews, your honest assessments and your undying support in everything that I set out to accomplish.

Preface

Implementing the requirements of ISO 9001 can be a daunting task for many organizations. In an attempt to develop a system that will pass the registration audit, we are tempted to establish processes with the primary purpose of complying with the requirements of ISO 9001. In doing so, however, it is easy to lose sight of the original intent of the standard—to continually improve the effectiveness of the quality management system at our organization.

This book is intended to help managers, management representatives, internal audit coordinators, and internal auditors implement a practical internal audit process that meets the requirements of ISO 9001:2000 while adding significant, measurable value to the organization's bottom line. The tools, techniques and step-by-step guidelines provided in this book can also be used by those organizations that have a well-established internal audit process but are looking for easy ways to make that process more effective. The tools in the appendices of this book have also been provided on the enclosed CD to facilitate your customizing them to fit the specific needs of your organization.

Perhaps the greatest impediment to a truly effective internal audit process is the notion that internal audits should mimic the external audit. We send our internal auditors to Lead Assessor training to learn how to conduct audits. We then use the external auditors as role models with respect to audit preparation, conducting the audit and reporting the audit. The external auditors are, as a rule, extremely professional and quite capable of achieving their desired result. But we fail to appreciate the significant difference in the purpose of the internal audits versus the external audits and thus fail to achieve the huge benefits that can be derived from the internal audit process.

It is my desire that this book will:

- Enable the reader to create an environment where management and employees fully appreciate the value of internal audits in the continual improvement of their organization and thus contribute to their success.

- Provide specific, easy-to-use tools and methods for audit preparation to enable the auditor to dig deeper into the effectiveness of processes and discover findings that will genuinely contribute to the success of the organization.

- Provide techniques that can be used in conducting the audit to tap into the vast expertise of the auditee and find those opportunities for improvement that will result in a significant return on investment.

- Provide specific methods and tools to report internal audit results in a way that encourages timely, thorough corrective action.

Numerous internal auditors have used the tools and techniques presented in this book to conduct the process-based internal audits that are encouraged by the requirements of ISO 9001:2000. When they followed the step-by-step preparation guidelines provided in Chapter 5, most brand new auditors conducted audits that were equally effective or perhaps even more effective than many audits performed by experienced quality management system professionals. Significant returns on investment have been calculated on audit findings discovered by first-time auditors using the tools, techniques, and methods described in this book!

I hope you will find that using these concepts will indeed make auditing to ISO 9001:2000 both easy and effective. Enjoy your journey!

CHAPTER 1

Introduction to Internal Auditing for ISO 9001:2000

In helping numerous companies implement the requirements of ISO 9001 since 1989, I have had the privilege of being a part of internal audit processes in a wide range of organizations and facilities. My clients have ranged from small janitorial businesses to global manufacturing companies; from large government agencies to small carton manufacturers. Many organizations develop internal audit processes that fully meet the requirements of ISO 9001 but achieve little else, while others have learned the art of using internal audits to achieve great successes in their business with a resulting positive impact on their bottom line.

I have studied both types of audit processes in an attempt to understand the secrets of truly successful internal auditing. I have found that audit processes that meet the requirements of ISO 9001, but achieve little else, have the following criteria in common:

- Management and employees view the internal audit process as a necessary evil to maintain the required certification.

- The organization establishes the internal audit process solely to ensure that it will pass the external audit;

- The stated purpose of the internal audit process is solely to comply with the requirements of ISO 9001 or other standard applicable to the organization (QS-9000, ISO/TS 16949, etc.)

- Internal auditors emulate the external auditors in conducting their audits.

As a rule, these organizations have not yet grasped the difference between the internal audit and the external audit and thus have failed to achieve the vast benefits that can be derived from an effectively implemented internal audit process.

Those organizations in which internal auditing is used as a vital and effective tool in improving the business and its bottom line have a very different set of criteria in common. These organizations:

- Understand the value of the internal audit in improving the bottom line of the business;

- Differentiate the purpose of the internal audit from that of the external audit;

- Base their audits on the effectiveness of processes in the quality management system and the interaction of those processes versus compliance to the applicable standard;

- Provide specific tools to enable the internal auditor to conduct audits that are successful in improving the business and its bottom line.

It is my sincere objective in this book to share with management personnel, management representatives, internal audit coordinators, and internal auditors the secrets of successful internal auditing and to provide the specific tools and techniques to make it happen.

Purpose of the internal audit

ISO 9000:2000 defines an audit as a "systematic, independent and documented process for obtaining audit evidence and evaluating it objectively to determine the extent to which audit criteria are fulfilled." This is certainly true of any audit—whether it is an internal audit, a supplier audit, or an ISO 9001 registration audit. But the purpose of each type of audit is somewhat unique.

The primary purpose of an ISO 9001 registration audit is to verify that an organization has a quality management system in place that meets the stated requirements of ISO 9001:2000. The registrar is specifically trained not to interject their opinions or recommend solutions to system problems. Their job is to carefully compare documentation, records, and activities to the requirements of ISO 9001:2000 and verify compliance to the standard. Though the auditors seek information from the auditee, they primarily work independently to evaluate the level of compliance to the standard. Auditees are wisely encouraged by the organization to simply answer the question that is asked and then quietly wait for the next question. Auditees are not encouraged to volunteer information to the registrar.

The purpose of a supplier audit is to verify that the supplier has systems and processes in place to ensure that the customer's specific requirements can be met. The auditors again evaluate documents, records, and activities to ensure that stated quality management system requirements are met as well as specified product or service requirements. The auditees are again advised not to volunteer any information beyond answering those questions that the auditor specifically asks.

Those organizations that have learned the secret of successful internal auditing have discovered that the internal audit is a different animal than the external audit, and that it should be performed in a different manner. In these organizations, the primary purpose of the audit is to find opportunities for improvement and the secondary purpose is to maintain the ISO 9001 registration. The internal auditor brings only half the knowledge to the table that is required for a successful audit—familiarity with the standard, knowledge of the organization's documentation, and a fresh perspective. The auditee brings the other half of the required knowledge—the expertise on the process being audited. The two parties are encouraged to work together to identify those processes that are not functioning at their best so that action can be taken to improve them. Such an approach to internal auditing requires a significant culture change in most organizations. Techniques to achieve that culture change are discussed in Chapter 2.

Objectives of the audit

There are four primary objectives of the internal audit:

- To verify conformance to applicable standards;
- To verify conformance to documented procedures;
- To verify effectiveness of the processes in the system;
- To identify opportunities to improve the system.

In implementing ISO 9001:1994, many organizations emphasized primarily the first two objectives. Audits focused on verifying whether or not the organization conformed to the requirements of ISO 9001 and whether or not activities within the organization conformed to its own documented procedures and instructions.

As the quality management system matured and nonconformances decreased, some organizations sought to make their internal audits more effective. These organizations began to focus more on the third and fourth objectives. Audits still verified conformance to ISO 9001 and to the organization's own documented procedures, but auditors were also trained to evaluate the health of the processes within the system. Employees were encouraged to work with the auditors to determine specific opportunities for improvement. Internal auditors were transformed from police figures to continual improvement facilitators. In doing so, internal audits began to generate findings that resulted in substantial, measurable improvements to the business.

ISO 9001:2000 further encourages this approach to internal auditing. Processes within the quality management system must be identified along with their sequence and interactions. (Reference 4.1.a/b, and 4.2.2.c) Criteria and methods must be determined to ensure that the operation and control of these processes are effective. (Reference 4.1.c) It would then make sense for the internal audits to focus on the effectiveness of these processes and identify where interactions may be breaking down. The best source of information on the where processes can be improved is the auditee—the expert on the process. Auditees should be encouraged to share their knowledge during the internal audit and thus play a vital role in the internal audit process.

Benefits of an effective audit process

There are numerous benefits of an effective internal audit program. Those that have been expressed to me by many of my clients include the following.

- *Reduced operating costs through better efficiency, increased productivity, better planning, and reduced scrap and rework.* Some organizations have calculated actual return on investment on audit findings that have totaled well into seven and eight figures in annual returns. Calculating return on investment for internal audit findings is further discussed in Chapter 2.

- *Improved safety performance.* Though ISO 9001:2000 does not specifically address employee health and safety, the requirements of ISO 9001:2000 and the internal audit process can have a positive impact on safety performance. A good employee training process and well-written operating instructions contribute to an effective occupational health and safety management system. When these have been combined with the accountability that audits provide, many organizations have seen substantial improvements in their safety performance just from implementing an ISO 9001-based system.

  One client saw such a reduction in lost-time accidents as a result of their ISO 9001-based system that the Risk Assessment Officer for their insurance carrier called to say that he would be recommending ISO 9001 to all of his clients.

- *Improved customer satisfaction.* Of course the ultimate goal of any quality management system is improved customer satisfaction. Improved customer satisfaction often leads to an increased customer base. Higher levels of customer satisfaction also lead to reductions in customer complaints and returned product, both of which are costly to any organization in terms of manpower, freight charges, rework, and scrap.

- *Improved morale.* Many clients beginning their internal audit process will ask, "How do you put the words 'audit' and 'improved morale' on the same page without laughing out loud?" The answer is easy. When employees are encouraged to contribute to the audit process and they see improvements made based on their input, audits serve to empower the workforce instead of belittling them.

One client several years ago received a visit from their corporate vice president. During the opening meeting for the visit, the VP announced that the organization was going to nix their efforts to achieve ISO 9001 registration. There were just too many other priorities at that point to spend resources on ISO implementation. Following his opening meeting, the VP went on a plant tour. During that tour the operators in the plant talked the VP out of his decision! When I asked the operators what caused them to feel strongly enough about ISO that they would buck a corporate vice president, they responded, "The internal audits are the only things in this quality junk that have actually made a difference. We are finally seeing things fixed that have needed fixing for a long time. And now he wants to get rid of it!"

- *Reduced barriers between departments.* Unfortunately, poorly performed audits will actually build barriers between departments rather than reduce them. But well-performed audits will give employees a chance to work together who have not had that chance before. When someone from the production department audits the purchasing process, for example, there will be more understanding of what it takes to get supplies and materials in on time. Very rarely do people write "ASAP" on a Purchase Requisition after they have audited the purchasing process! When auditors from production see how the lab calibrates instrumentation, they will be less likely to request repeated retests. When the lab sees what it takes for production to pull a sample correctly, they will be less likely to request repeated resamples. Auditing increases the level of understanding of other departments throughout the organization.

- *Survival.* The ultimate benefit of any internal audit process is survival. Those organizations that have implemented a formal process for continual improvement are the organizations that are most likely to exist ten years from now. Internal auditing can be a powerful tool in any organization's continual improvement process.

The first step in developing a successful internal audit process is creating an environment where management and employees will buy into the audit process and contribute to its success. Techniques to create that environment are discussed in Chapter 2.

Selecting the right auditors for your internal audit team is the next step. Issues to consider in doing so are discussed in Chapter 3. Defining typical roles and responsibilities in the audit process is discussed in Chapter 4.

Chapter 5 outlines a step-by-step process to prepare for an internal audit. Preparation for the audit is the most important phase in ensuring its success. If auditors know in advance exactly what records they will be pulling, how many they will pull, and what they will be looking for when they pull them, they can go out confident that they will conduct a good audit. Tools are provided in the Appendices and on the enclosed CD to assist the auditors in ensuring their success.

In Chapter 6, we will learn how to conduct the audit in a way that encourages the auditees' input. We will talk about how to lead an effective opening meeting, how to establish the correct environment during the audit and how to handle difficult auditees.

Chapter 7 describes how to report the audit in a way that encourages timely, effective, and thorough corrective action. Though auditors are not responsible for the corrective action following an audit, there are four things they can do to encourage the auditees to undertake effective corrective action without undue delay. We will examine these four things in Chapter 7.

And finally in Chapter 8 we will look at how to follow up on audit findings to ensure that the corrective action was both implemented and effective. I hope you enjoy the book and get some valuable ideas to improve your internal audit process!

CHAPTER 2

Creating an Environment for Successful Audits

Gaining management's support
for the audit process

The single most important factor in the success of any quality improvement initiative is management's leadership. To solicit that leadership, we often present a series of presentations showing the tools and processes that would benefit the company. As it relates to auditing, we present a series of audit findings along with a list of those who have closed out their findings and those who have not. But this approach rarely creates the enthusiasm in the management team that is being sought. Management is paid to ensure the financial success of the organization. Speaking the language of money is critical to gaining the support and participation that is needed to make any quality improvement initiative succeed.

An effective internal audit process for ISO 9001:2000 involves evaluating the overall effectiveness of processes, not simply the organization's compliance to the standard and its own documented procedures. (Reference Chapter 5 for a description of techniques that may be used to audit process effectiveness.) Through evaluating processes and their interactions, an internal audit can pinpoint improvements that will increase the organization's efficiencies, productivity, and ultimate profitability. These findings may account for only 10-40% of the total number of discrepancies. But when recorded and corrected, the company should make every effort to quantify the successes and report them at management review.

The review of audit findings at a typical management review meeting will include a summary of audit findings, a status of corrective and preventive actions and perhaps an update on those required actions that have slipped past their estimated completion dates. To achieve the level of commitment that is necessary to ensure success of the audit process, the management representative needs to add an additional comment. "Of the 14 audit findings that were recorded in the second quarter, we have been able to calculate return on investment for 5 of them. It came to an annual savings of $952,675." Such an approach will generate a significantly higher level of interest.

The best method to cultivate the mindset of seeing return on investment in audit findings is to discuss specific findings in specific companies for which return on investment has been calculated and reported. Many of these findings are quite common and may even look familiar to many readers!

FINDING:

"There is no training process for new technical employees that affect product quality—i.e.: process engineers and lab chemists."

ISO 9001:2000 requires that the organization determine the necessary competence for personnel performing work affecting product quality and either provide training or take some other appropriate action to satisfy those needs. (Reference 6.2.2.a and 6.2.2.b in ISO 9001:2000.) Technical and management personnel often directly impact product quality but are frequently omitted from the training process.

The auditor could cite the finding as stated above and generate little enthusiasm in developing a training process for technical employees. Or the auditor could spend just a few minutes digging to see if the lack of such a process had actually impacted the effectiveness of engineering and lab-related processes. Where no training process exists for technical employees, brief conversations with new engineers or chemists could reveal significant errors that were made due to the employee not being familiar with specific product or process validation requirements, regulatory requirements, customer requirements, project management requirements, document control requirements, etc. In one recent audit, two quality system failures caused by the lack of training were documented at $250,000 for the first event and $1.2 million for the second.

The finding can then be documented as follows:

"There is no training process for technical employees affecting product quality—i.e.: process engineers and lab chemists. The lack of such a process was identified as a primary cause of two recent quality problems."

At the closing meeting, the auditor should report that the lack of identified competency requirements for technical employees and the lack of a process to meet those requirements is a discrepancy against 6.2.2.a and 6.2.2.b of the standard. But the auditor should then go on to state, "The lack of such a system was identified to be a primary cause of two breakdowns that cost the company a total of $1.45 million. If we could get our arms around this issue and prevent a similar occurrence in the future, it would be well worth our efforts."

FINDING:

"The Customer Specification Book in the lab is obsolete and not included on the Customer Service Department's distribution list for customer specifications."

Let's count how many things are wrong with this picture. ISO 9001:2000 requires that the organization revise relevant documents when product requirements are changed and that relevant personnel be made aware the changed requirements. (Reference 7.2.2) ISO 9001:2000 also requires that documents required by the quality management system must be under control. (Reference 4.2.3)

Several additional questions revealed that two of the previous five returned shipments were caused by obsolete specifications in the Customer Spec Book. In both instances, the corrective action simply involved updating the specific specs that were not current. (Does this sound familiar?) There was no additional effort to determine the cause of the problem and take action to keep it from recurring. (Reference 8.5.2.b) To have TWO shipments returned for the same reason and NOT ask, "WHY were the specs not current?" indicates that the organization does not fully understand the corrective action process. Further study of the corrective action process revealed that to be the case. But for the sake of this discussion, we will simply focus on the two returned shipments.

The finding can then be documented as follows:

"The Customer Specification Book in the lab is obsolete and not included on the Customer Service Department's distribution list for customer specifications. Two of the last five returned shipments met the specs available in the lab, but did not meet the new specs that had been agreed upon by Customer Service."

The cost of the two returned shipments—including freight charges, unloading into dedicated containers, rework of the nonconforming product, and premium freight charges for re-shipment—totaled $86,000. Of course the hard costs did not include the damage to reputation and customer satisfaction. Simply updating the Customer Specification Book and asking Customer Service to add this site's laboratory to their distribution list for customer specifications would prevent similar mishaps from occurring in the future.

FINDING:

"Three of the five prints reviewed at the construction site
were at least two revisions out of date."

Document control is a requirement of ISO 9001:2000 that is often considered to be a necessary evil to achieve registration. But in this engineering and construction firm, problems related to print control proved to be the number one cause of exceptions noted by the customer during the project closure phase, costing the organization a lot of money in rework. Just a few additional questions uncovered 26 exceptions resulting in rework that were caused by the lack of print control.

The finding can then be documented as follows:

"Three of the five prints reviewed at the construction site
were at least two revisions out of date. A total of 26
customer exceptions on the previous project were found to
be related to print control problems."

Print control at a construction site is a difficult beast to tame. Controlling the interfaces between design engineers, the drafting department, and the construction crew is a daunting task. But reducing exceptions due to print control by just 20% would result in a significant savings for the organization. For many projects, this could account for five percent or more of the total project costs.

FINDING:

"Procedure PR-02 requires that the Production Scheduler
forward a production plan to the Purchasing Department

two weeks prior to the production run. Purchasing is not receiving the production plan until two to three days prior to each run."

Further questions revealed that the delay in planning information had resulted in numerous late shipments of raw materials. Costs associated with the late shipments included:

- 29 lost production hours
- Premium freight charges to expedite the arrival of raw materials
- Premium freight charges for final product to meet the customer's delivery requirements
- Costs associated with unplanned changeovers in production to expedite runs in order to meet the customer's delivery requirements

The finding can then be documented as follows:

"Procedure PR-02 requires that the Manufacturing Scheduler forward a production plan to the Purchasing Department two weeks prior to the production run. Purchasing is not receiving the production plan until two to three days prior to each run. In the past three months, late delivery of raw materials has resulted in 29 hours of lost production time, excess premium freight charges, and costs associated with excess changeovers."

Of course system breakdowns of this magnitude are rarely the fault of one person. Optimizing the planning process in this organization required a cross-functional team of employees who were well trained in root cause analysis and problem-solving techniques. But their efforts resulted in a net return on investment of over $400,000 annually. Another success for the internal audit process!

In evaluating the return on investment for audit findings, typical sources of savings may include:

- Production time
- Reduced scrap/rework
- Productivity improvements
- Premium freight
- Costs associated with customer complaints and returned goods
- Costs associated with design verification and validation failures
- Costs associated with employee turnover
- Costs associated with excess inspection and testing
- Excess inventory costs
- Spare parts for equipment maintenance

Of course, not all internal audit findings will result in such financial benefits. But focusing on the effectiveness of processes in addition to conformance to applicable standards and procedures should result in 10-40% of audit findings that will generate significant return on investment. Quantifying and communicating the successes associated with the internal audit process will generate not only support for the process, but perhaps even enthusiasm for the process.

Gaining employees' support for the audit process

The people who know best where processes and their interactions are implemented effectively are the people closest to the work. The Maintenance Technician knows better than anyone whether or not the Preventive Maintenance process is effective. The Design Engineer knows better than anyone whether the design process is working effectively and where the opportunities for improvement lie. To effectively audit these processes, the auditor needs to gain the support of the auditee. The auditee needs to understand that he/she plays a vital role in the internal audit process.

The best place to start in ensuring that the auditee understands his/her role in the audit process is to provide some basic training. This training is not typically time-consuming and can simply be an agenda item at a regularly scheduled employee meeting, department meeting or "brown-bag" lunch. The agenda for this training may include:

- *What is the purpose of an internal audit?*

  An informal survey of employees in a cross-section of industries has shown that more than 95% of employees believe that the internal audit is intended to catch them doing something wrong or to catch them not doing something they are supposed to do. As an opening exercise in my audit classes, I write the word "audit" on a flip chart pad and ask the participants to yell out their first thoughts. The printable responses often include:

❑ IRS

❑ Fear

❑ Intimidation

❑ Someone else coming out here telling me how to do my job

❑ Pink slip

❑ Vacation

❑ Hide and seek

❑ Clipboard (now this one speaks volumes!)

Rarely do employees yell out "continual improvement!" or "the best thing that's ever happened to my organization!"

Many internal auditors believe that the primary purpose of the internal audit is simply to conform to the requirements of ISO 9001:2000. (OUCH!) Indeed, ISO 9001:2000 does require that internal audits be performed. But employees and auditors alike need to understand their intended purpose.

As discussed in the previous chapter, the primary purpose of an internal audit is to get better at how we do business. The auditor only brings half of the required knowledge to the table. The auditor should bring an understanding of the applicable standard, knowledge of the documented procedures, and a fresh set of eyes to the process. But in an internal audit, the auditee brings the other half of the knowledge required to perform a successful audit. The auditee brings expertise on the process being audited, how that process actually operates on a day-to-day basis, and where the major opportunities for improvement may exist. When all participants truly understand what the organization can accomplish through the internal audit process, the auditee will be less likely to run when the auditor enters the department.

- *Who is the customer of the audit process?*

  A common response to this question is, "Audits don't have customers, do they? Audits have victims!"

  Most employees have never really thought of an internal audit as having customers. Of course the textbook answer is that the customer of an internal audit is management. The audit provides management with information necessary to evaluate conformance to the required quality management system standard and to identify opportunities for continual improvement.

  But, indeed, the auditee is also a primary customer of the audit. If employees do not have:

  ❑ Required tools
  ❑ Required information

❑ Adequate training

❑ Suitable instructions or other documentation

and if these resources are provided as the result of an audit, the employee is truly a customer of this process. Employees need to see themselves as active participants and beneficiaries of this process in order to contribute their much-needed expertise.

- *How open should employees be during the internal audit?*

  The answer to this question becomes obvious when the purpose of the internal audit is truly understood. If the organization is indeed using the internal audit process to improve the business, employees should be encouraged to help the auditor in any way possible to identify potential failures in the system. The auditee provides the expertise on the process being audited. To identify breakdowns in the interfaces between processes, it is critical to get the input of the auditee.

  Should an organization allow punitive action following an internal audit? This is a tough question in some industries, but most organizations should make it clear that there will be no punitive action based on audit results. See "After the Audit" below for a complete discussion of punitive action following an internal audit.

- What will happen with the audit results?

  Employees need to understand what will happen with the audit results. Typically the results will be reviewed at a closing meeting where management of the area audited will be given a chance to question the findings for understanding and perhaps even begin the corrective action process. A Corrective Action Request (or your organization's equivalent) will be initiated to document the cause of the finding, the action taken to remove the cause, and what was done to ensure that the action taken was effective.

The awareness training should lay a good foundation for employees to understand the intent of the audit process.

The internal auditor can also contribute to the efforts to gain employees' support for the audit process. The auditor should make it clear that he/she respects the auditee's expertise in the area being audited. The auditees should be invited to bring out any issues that they would like to see in the audit report to ensure that they get the attention they deserve. Partnering with the auditee in the audit process will empower the workforce and add more value to the audit results.

After the audit

Should punitive action be allowed following an internal audit? This is a difficult question that should be discussed within an organization prior to the first audit. Punitive action can range from a supervisor chastising an employee for allowing a finding to be recorded to terminating an employee based on audit results. When evaluating whether or not punitive action should be allowed—or to what degree it should be allowed—the organization should consider the impact that action would have on the quality of future audits.

In a recent audit at a client's facility, an operator confessed to the auditor that he indeed shipped nonconforming product on a routine basis. In this industry, quality control inspectors are not common. The operators are expected to perform product inspections for the products they produce. Upon further questioning by the auditor, the operator stated that the company pays him to ship nonconforming product. He said, "Man, my base pay is minimum wage and I have five kids to feed. I get bonus pay for every product that goes on that pallet. I can assure you that if I make it, it goes on the pallet—good or bad."

To verify this issue with objective evidence, the auditor visited the shipping department. Seven percent of the product staged to be shipped was obviously nonconforming. Based on this evidence, the auditor wrote a finding that stated, "The incentive system encourages the shipment of nonconforming product."

Upon hearing the finding, the Production Superintendent became quite angry. Slamming his fist on table, he yelled, "I want the operator codes off those products!" The auditor quietly pulled the Production Superintendent aside and explained that the operator was not the problem. The incentive system was the problem. The nonconforming products were not isolated to a single person.

With the correct focus, the organization redesigned the incentive system. The bonus pay for each product was actually increased slightly, but each returned product resulted in the appropriate operator's losing 100 points. If the operator shipped only acceptable product, his pay was actually increased by about 4%. Customer satisfaction ratings soared and the company calculated a huge return on investment based on eliminating the causes of nonconforming product, fewer returned shipment costs and increased business with their largest customers. These successes would have never been possible if the Production Superintendent had been allowed to continue his original response.

In most situations, not allowing punitive action is an easy decision if the organization is truly trying to create an environment of open communication between the auditor and the auditee. But what action should be taken, for example, if the internal auditor discovers falsified records? In most organizations, falsified records are grounds for termination.

Some companies take the stand that there are other processes in place to address personnel performance and disciplinary issues. The internal quality system audit is not the tool to identify these problems. If the organization is depending on an annual quality system audit to identify such problems, it has bigger problems than the individual employee. The supervisory or management system is not effective.

In many cases, falsified records are not unique to an individual. Where audits are conducted at 10:00 a.m. and the auditor discovers production log sheets completed through the end of the shift, this practice will probably be found at more than one workstation. Where this practice has been allowed to continue throughout the organization, the problem runs deeper than employee discipline. In investigating the root cause, the organization may consider the following:

- Is there any value to the data? Operational personnel apparently do not appreciate its value. It may be possible that someone got a little overly enthusiastic in implementing the requirements of ISO 9001:2000 and is requiring the documentation of information that is of no value to the organization. This could represent an opportunity to streamline the process.

- Have employees traditionally been held accountable to following procedures and recording data? Depending on the industry, employees may not have been held accountable for following procedures and recording data before ISO 9001. In one audit, employees had consistently recorded the same number on all their log sheets. When I asked numerous operators why they recorded the same number on each log sheet, I got the same answer from each one. If the results are within process specs, their supervisors had told them to record the target. The supervisors thought it would look better in customer audits. Hmm.

- Are adequate resources available to generate required data? In one instance where I discovered falsified data, a little further investigation found that operators were supposed to sample the product every hour, run the sample to the lab (about a five minute walk), test the sample and return to the production line to record the results on the production log sheet. If the process were running smoothly, it was possible to get this done. But if the operator was needed to resolve process upsets, he/she could not leave the area to perform the required inspection. For years, operators recorded "busy" on the log sheet instead of the test results. When a new production manager threatened jobs if the required testing was not completed, test results began to get recorded every hour. Interesting!

• How is this data being used and by whom? In some organizations, the data is critical to the effective evaluation of the process. Who is responsible for analyzing this data and what decisions are made based on this information? These issues should be addressed in employee training sessions and supervisors should ensure the accuracy of the data throughout the year.

Where the practice of falsified records is rampant throughout the organization, the auditor should identify the practice so that the root cause can be determined and eliminated.

Where the issues that we have just discussed have been resolved and employees fully understand the consequences of falsified data, some organizations will clearly communicate to employees that punitive action will not be allowed following the audit—unless there is a blatant, intentional disregard for established policies, like falsifying records. This approach is mandatory in certain regulated industries (i.e. medical products or aerospace industries). But the rules need to be clearly communicated throughout the organization before the first audit so that there is no misunderstanding.

The bottom line is that an organization should clearly establish and communicate the policy relative to punitive action based on audit results. To the extent that punitive action is allowed, vital input from the auditee will be lost and internal audits will lose potential value.

How does a company overcome punitive action from previous audits in trying to create a more open environment in the internal audit process? A creative thought that has been successful in some organizations is to issue two reports following an audit. The first is issued only to the manager responsible for corrective action and to the management representative, who is typically responsible for tracking the status of corrective actions. This report includes the audit findings and is the traditional audit report that will be evaluated by the registrar.

About 60 days following the audit, a second report is issued. This report describes only the successes that have resulted from the last internal audit. It describes those actions that have been taken to improve the quality system, its processes, and the product or service. This report is issued to top management and touts the successes of the audit rather than the failures of the system.

In addition to better communicating the successes of the internal audit process, this approach also encourages timely, thorough corrective action. If the responsible manager knows that what he/she is able to accomplish in that 60-day period will be communicated to the rest of the staff, it encourages not only a timely response, but also a thorough response. Communicating the successes resulting from the internal audit process is critical to gaining the support of both management personnel and employees.

CHAPTER 3

Selecting and Maintaining the Internal Audit Team

Is your audit pool adequately staffed?

There is no perfect number of auditors an organization must have to perform effective internal audits. Some organizations, particularly those in the medical and aerospace industries, are fortunate enough to have fulltime internal auditors. Most, however, call upon employees who are already overloaded in their current positions to add internal auditing to their list of responsibilities.

The number of auditors you will need to train will depend on:

- The size of your organization

- The type of product or service produced

- How you define the scope of each audit

About the only incorrect answer would be to train one auditor. Who will audit the internal audit process? Who will audit the other activities performed by the auditor? Unless your organization plans to outsource some or all of the internal audit process, you will need to train at least two auditors.

Other than that, a general rule of thumb is to have enough qualified auditors in your auditor pool so that any one auditor is not called upon to perform more than one audit a quarter. Where internal auditors are asked to squeeze an audit into their already full calendars each month, the audits are often quite shallow and do not go to the depths that will result in findings that generate a return on investment.

Many organizations will define an audit schedule that requires one or two processes to be audited each month. (See Chapter 4 for a full discussion on the scope of each audit and the scheduling process.) If you have chosen this schedule and if your organization has a procedure that requires audits to be conducted by two auditors, that would necessitate at least six trained auditors. Where you think you will need six, train at least ten. Some employees will love auditing, but others will hate it. With only one exception, I have found that auditors who hate auditing typically do not perform very thorough audits. Let those who do not enjoy it leave the audit team.

What job functions should be represented in the audit pool?

Some audits will require specific expertise in order to be effective. An audit of the quality planning process in the automotive industry, for example, will require some expertise in Failure Mode and Effects Analysis (FMEA), Production Part

Approval Process (PPAP), and Advanced Product Quality Planning (APQP) methodologies. An audit of statistical process control will require some basic knowledge of the proper use of statistical process control (SPC). But any employee from any department in the organization may perform most other audits of the quality management system.

The internal audit pool should not be staffed with employees from only the quality department. This approach will encourage the concept that ISO 9001 is a "quality department" standard. In reality, ISO 9001 is more of a business management standard that impacts the entire organization. As such, the auditors should be chosen from throughout the organization.

Selecting auditors from each department in the organization, if possible, will create champions of the ISO 9001 system throughout the company. Typically the internal auditors appreciate the value of the quality management system and the audit process more than any other employee. With a trained auditor in each department, employees can hear from peers that the audit process is a great chance to initiate action where they know action is needed.

Selecting auditors from each department also provides a trained set of eyes throughout the organization that can unofficially look for system failures throughout the year—not just at audit time.

What personal attributes make good internal auditors?

ISO/DIS 19011, Guidelines for quality and/or environmental management systems auditing, outlines the key personal attributes of an effective auditor. In selecting candidates for the internal auditor pool, the organization should consider those that demonstrate the following attributes:

- *Ethical* — fair, truthful, sincere, honest and discreet. Auditing involves the investigation of actions taken by fellow employees. The effective internal auditor is one that employees feel comfortable talking with and can trust to handle audit findings appropriately.

- *Open-minded* — willing to consider alternative ideas or points of view. Quite often the auditor will find processes that are implemented in ways that are far different than the processes in their own particular department. The immediate response is, "This is different than anything I have seen before. It must be a finding." Even registrars struggle with this reaction. In reality, if the process being audited conforms to the standard and the organization's own documentation and if the evidence shows that it is effective, there is no finding. The auditor is not being paid that day to express his/her opinion of the process. The auditor's job is to compare facts and data to the standard, to verify conformance to documented procedures, and to evaluate the effectiveness of that process.

- *Diplomatic* — tactful in dealing with people. Perhaps the greatest attribute of an internal auditor is the ability to treat others with dignity and respect. The auditor must recognize the expertise of the auditee in the daily operation of the process being audited. As findings are uncovered, the auditor must report those findings in a diplomatic manner that respects the expertise of the auditee.

- *Observant* — constantly and actively aware of physical surroundings and activities. The effective auditor must be observant of activities around him and not focus only on those questions on the checklist. The checklist is intended to be a guideline to ensure that basic requirements are covered. It is not intended to be used as a script for the audit. The internal auditor should follow through on activities that prove interesting and worth pursuing.

- *Perceptive* — instinctively aware of and able to understand and adapt to situations. Often the audit will lead into paths that were not anticipated by the auditor. The effective auditor will pursue those paths where they may lead to opportunities for continual improvement.

I would like to add a few more:

- *Persistent and thorough.* It is NOT the responsibility of the internal auditor to determine the root cause of findings. It may take experts in the process several months of investigation to identify the true root cause of some system failures. But if the auditor suspects the cause and can verify that cause in less than an hour, the auditor should pursue the issue to assist in the corrective action process.

An example of this trait is illustrated by the auditor that found about 10% of incoming component parts being scrapped in production. A quick visit to the receiving department showed that the scrapped parts fully met the requirements on the print. Something wasn't right. A call to engineering verified that the print in receiving was two revisions out of date. Less than thirty minutes of investigation revealed that the cause of the problem was that the supplier and receiving had been inadvertently omitted from engineering's distribution list for revised prints.

- *Curious*. I tell my husband that I love auditing because it allows me to learn new processes and expand my horizons. He says, "Bull, honey, you're just nosey." Okay. Call it what you will. But an excellent trait for an internal auditor is curiosity about how processes work—a desire to trace a process from the beginning to the end to verify that interfaces have been well defined and implemented.

If I could summarize the desired personal attributes of an internal auditor, it would be the ability to treat others with dignity and respect. In selecting internal auditors, this personal attribute is more important than the individual's technical knowledge of the processes in the organization. Competencies related to the technical skills of auditing can be provided through training, practice audits, and the provision of appropriate audit tools. Effective audit tools are discussed in Chapter 5. Examples of these tools are provided in the appendices in this book.

How can an organization maintain the audit pool?

Clients often ask me to perform "refresher training" for their internal audit team. Upon my arrival each year at a few clients' facilities, I see a brand new set of bright individuals anxious to learn new audit techniques. I began to get curious about why the experienced auditors were not present from year to year.

In talking with some of those experienced auditors, I heard comments like, "I spend several hours preparing for an audit and get chewed out by my manager for letting my work slide a little. I then go into an area to conduct the audit and get chewed out by that manager for finding system failures. Then I report the findings at the closing meeting and get further chewed out for reporting those findings. Help me understand again why I should enjoy this."

Of course, these issues are indicative of an organization that needs to work harder on establishing the right environment for the audit process. (See Chapter 2) Beyond that, however, the management representative should make some effort to encourage and maintain the audit team. Specific actions may include:

- Sending the auditor a personal note expressing sincere appreciation for a job well done. In teaching classes across the country, I often ask how many participants have ever received a personal note from someone in their organization expressing appreciation for work they have done. Of the few that raise their hands, I then ask how many still have that note. Over 90% of those that have received the note still have it! That illustrates what a small token of appreciation means to the recipient.

- Providing tangible reinforcements that express appreciation for the time spent in the audit process. Organizations often provide a "company dinner" for the auditors and their guests. But we are then asking them to spend yet more hours away from private time with their families. Presenting the auditors with a $50 gift certificate to a nice restaurant of their choice is typically more appreciated. The message here is that you recognize that the auditors may have spent their own time preparing for and reporting the audit and that you are giving them some quality time back with their spouses, families, or significant others.

- Recognizing audit responsibilities in performance evaluations. Auditing provides a significant benefit to the organization and should be recognized in the auditor's performance evaluation.

One of the greatest challenges in performing successful internal audits is finding the time to adequately prepare for and conduct the audit. The preparation process is described in more detail in Chapter 5. It requires studying the standard that is being examined, studying any documentation for the process being audited, and creating a good checklist to ensure that the quality management system is thoroughly covered. Even with the appropriate tools being provided to the auditor, preparing to audit a single process can take several hours. Where can we carve out that much time?

If we try to squeeze time into an already full schedule to prepare for an audit, we rarely make it happen. But if we have committed to spend time with someone else, the odds of making it happen increase. The perfect example here is starting an exercise program. If you try to work exercise into your day, time seems to get away before the exercise takes place. But if we commit to meet a friend each morning or at lunch to walk, we typically make the time to be there.

If several processes are being audited in a given month or quarter, plan an audit preparation meeting. The applicable auditors can then meet in a conference room where they can help each other prepare for the audits. Auditors will have a chance to bounce questions off each other to see if they are worded correctly. They can discuss the interpretation of the standard, where it may be in question, or ask questions of other auditors in the room that may be more familiar with the process being audited. If the meeting takes place over the lunch hour, make sure that a lunch is provided for the auditors.

Selecting the right auditors and maintaining an experienced audit team are important elements in an effective internal audit process.

CHAPTER 4

Typical Responsibilities and Authorities in the Audit Process

Management representative / audit coordinator

The management representative, or a delegated audit coordinator, is responsible for administrating and coordinating the audit process. Typical responsibilities associated with this position are described below.

Select the audit team

ISO 9001:2000 specifies that auditors cannot audit their own work. It further states the auditors must be selected to ensure the "objectivity and impartiality" of the audit process. (Reference 8.2.2 in ISO 9001:2000.) So the management representative must select auditors that are not directly responsible for the process being audited.

Management representatives often try to walk this line closely. The thinking is, "I'll select Bob to audit the maintenance process. He used to work in Maintenance three years ago and knows the department well enough to know where to look for the breakdowns." On the surface, this sounds like excellent reasoning. But in reality, the best internal audits are typically performed by those that know the least about the process. Remember that the auditor brings to the audit their knowledge of the standard and knowledge of the organization's own documented procedures. It is the auditee that brings expertise on the process being audited. With that in mind, the auditor does not need technical expertise in the processes being audited. Indeed, the more the auditor "knows" about the process being audited, the more he/she is likely to audit on the basis of their opinion of that process rather than the documented requirements.

Many organizations require that two auditors rather than one perform each audit. Again, there is no "correct" response to this issue, but there are advantages and disadvantages of each choice. The advantages of auditing in pairs include:

- *It provides a training mechanism for new auditors.* New or inexperienced auditors can partner with experienced auditors to provide a mechanism for "on-the-job" training.

- *It provides a second opinion on audit findings.* Many internal auditors do not get enough audit experience to feel completely comfortable making judgments on their own. They often appreciate having a second auditor present who hears and sees the same things and can help make decisions on what should be cited as a finding and what should not be.

- *It provides for a note-taker and a question-asker.* Many internal auditors find it difficult to actively listen to the auditee, understand the process, follow-up on interesting issues, and take notes that they can read at this time tomorrow. Using two auditors allows one to keep up with legible notes while one can focus on the issues being discussed.

But, of course, there are disadvantages associated with using two auditors:

- *Two auditors can be more intimidating to the auditee than one.* Should the organization want to take advantage of the benefits of auditing in pairs, the intimidation factor can be easily diminished. The note-taker should stand or sit in such a way that the auditee can read the notes as they are being written. This would require that one auditor sit or stand with the auditee while the other auditor faces them to ask the questions. The auditors should invite the auditee to read the notes as they are written so that the notes belong to the three participants and not just the two auditors.

- *The two auditors may tend to talk over each other and leave little room for the auditee to contribute to the conversation.* This can be overcome by ensuring that each auditor understands his or her role at any given time. There is a question-asker and a note-taker at all times. These roles can be changed throughout the audit to give both auditors a chance to participate equally in both roles. When the question-asker reaches the end of his train of thought, he turns to the note-taker and says "Take it home. Have I missed anything or do you have anything else to add?" At that point the note-taker has the floor. Any questions that have not been addressed on the checklist can be addressed at that time.

The decision to use one auditor or two will depend on:

- The experience of the auditors
- The type of auditor (full-time or part-time)
- The scope of the audit
- The complexity of the process being audited

A final issue that may come up in selecting auditors is whether or not to use top management personnel as internal auditors. Again, there are advantages and disadvantages. If a top manager wants to spend two days of their time to attend internal audit training and another two days to prepare for, conduct, and issue a report for a process audit, the employees will inevitably notice management's commitment to the quality management system. But the presence of a manager during the audit may be quite intimidating to the auditee. If the auditee is shut out of the audit process, you will lose half the knowledge that is required for a successful audit.

Here is a suggestion. If a manager would like to serve as an internal auditor, first hold a small celebration in honor of the fact that you work for a manager who is truly committed to the quality management system. Then ask the manager to partner with an auditor that is not on the management team. The manager should be the note-taker at first and allow the partner to be the question-asker. If the auditees tend to cut their eyes at the manager before answering the questions or, even worse, direct the answer to the manager, that would indicate that the auditees are seeking the manager's approval in their answer. The manager should then back off the audit team and show their support for the process in other ways.

Determine the scope of the audit

The most difficult activity in administrating the internal audit is defining the scope of each audit. There are primarily three ways to audit an organization:

- *Audit the entire organization at one time.* This is the type of audit performed by the registrar or "corporate" internal auditors. They will audit every process in the quality management system throughout the organization so that they can verify that the interfaces between those processes are well defined and effectively implemented.

  This type of internal audit, however, is not typically recommended for organizations with greater than 25 employees. For larger organizations, the scope is so large that the sample sizes become very small and there is rarely time to follow up on interesting issues. The audit is also quite difficult to prepare for if the auditors are not extremely knowledgeable of the standard. Each auditor will have to read, study and understand five or six sections of ISO 9001 as well as the supporting documentation for each section. That can be quite time-consuming.

- *Audit by department, area, or product.* In this type of audit, every applicable process within the area or department is included in the scope of the audit. For example, an audit of the Purchasing Department might include requirements related to:

  ❑ The policy statement and supporting objectives

  ❑ Control of documents

  ❑ Control of records

  ❑ Definition of responsibilities and authorities

  ❑ Training of purchasing personnel

  ❑ The evaluation, selection, and re-evaluation of suppliers

  ❑ Placing orders for purchased goods and services

  ❑ Handling nonconforming purchased goods

  ❑ Supplier corrective action

Or an organization may select a specific product and audit each process that is related to the production of that product. In this type of audit, the auditor may select a specific lot number, batch number, or part number of the final product and audit the processes that related to that product:

❏ Handling and storage of the product (if it is still available at the site)

❏ Product traceability

❏ Final product inspection and testing

❏ In-process inspection and testing

❏ Control of process parameters while the product was being made

❏ Incoming inspection and testing of raw materials or component parts that went into that specific product

❏ Supplier qualification for the suppliers of incoming materials that went into that product

❏ Employee training for those that dealt with that product

❏ Document control of procedures, instructions, specifications, drawings, etc. related to that product

These types of audits were quite common for organizations conforming to ISO 9001:1994, but will be more difficult for those organizations seeking conformance with ISO 9001:2000. ISO 9001:2000 focuses more on the processes in the quality management system and the interaction of those processes. To audit each of the processes in these audits and verify that the interactions with other processes are effectively implemented requires auditing skills and knowledge that an internal auditor may not get the experience to develop.

Audit preparation for these audits can also be very difficult for new or inexperienced auditors, as it requires an excellent knowledge of the standard or plenty of time to prepare for the audit. Auditing the effectiveness of interfaces between the processes being studied can also be more difficult if the audit is to remain within a single area or department.

In very large organizations or organizations that are spread out over a large geographical area, these audits will become more practical. But the auditors must be especially conscious of their responsibility to verify that process interfaces involving other departments are effectively implemented. Methods to verify process interfaces are discussed further in Chapter 5.

- *Audit by process in the quality management system.* This type of audit focuses on a single process within the quality management system. An audit of the purchasing process, for example, would include verifying that inputs into the purchasing process have been clearly defined, communicated, and/or implemented and that outputs provide evidence that the process is effectively implemented. Inputs into the purchasing process may include:

❑ Well-defined requirements for purchased products (perhaps in the form of raw material specifications, prints or drawings). These requirements are typically provided by the design function.

❑ Timely production or service planning needs to be able to meet suppliers' specified lead times. These requirements are typically provided by the manufacturing group or service providers.

❑ Clearly defined pricing policies provided by management.

❑ An effective purchasing software program, if applicable, typically provided and/or maintained by the information systems group.

❑ Clearly defined evaluation, selection and re-evaluation criteria for suppliers. Purchasing, quality, design, and/or manufacturing personnel often jointly develop these criteria.

❑ Well-understood organizational and departmental objectives impacting the purchasing process. Top management typically provides organizational objectives; departmental management then identifies departmental objectives to support the organizational objectives.

To verify the outputs of the purchasing process, the auditor should verify that incoming products are consistently arriving on time and within established specification ranges. An audit of the purchasing process will then require that receiving personnel and users of the purchased products are included in the scope of the audit.

The process audit will also verify that responsibilities and authorities have been clearly defined in the process, that documentation is available to control the process where needed (reference 4.2.1.d in ISO 9001:2000) and that activities conform with the requirements of that documentation.

Focusing on a single process allows the auditor to fully verify that the interfaces between that process and other processes have been clearly defined and are effectively implemented. Because the majority of system breakdowns occur between processes, most of the audit findings that generate good opportunities for business improvement are found when verifying these interfaces. It is for this reason that process audits are the primary focus of this book. Tools and techniques to prepare for and to conduct effective process audits are outlined in Chapters 5 and 6.

The management representative, or designated audit coordinator, should clearly define what processes are to be covered in each audit as well as what areas or departments must be included. Whether the organization audits by area/ department or by process, a matrix similar to that provided in

Appendix D is an excellent tool to communicate the scope of each audit to the appropriate auditors.

After the entire system has been covered in an initial audit, the organization may choose to provide for more focused attention on those areas that need it. An "X" on the matrix in Appendix D indicates that the specified department or area is critical to the successful implementation of the process and must be audited every time that process is audited. An "O" or an "E" indicates that the specified department or area plays a more peripheral role in the process and can be audited every other year. (The "O" indicates that it is audited during the odd numbered years and the "E" indicates that it is audited during the even numbered years.) ISO 9001:2000 allows for such a schedule when it states in 8.2.2 that audits must be planned based on "the status and importance of an activity." Note that this matrix also ensures that each process is audited each year and that each department or area is audited each year. Though not a specified requirement in ISO 9001:2000, it is good business practice for most organizations and highly encouraged by many registrars.

The matrix in Appendix D is intended to get you started on developing one for your company. As with any tool provided with this book, the matrix will need to be customized to reflect the specific requirements of your quality management system.

Establish the schedule, time, and duration of the audit

The management representative typically schedules the general timeframe for the audit as well as the duration of the audit. Though the specific practices may differ depending upon the organization, most companies develop and issue an annual internal audit schedule in December or January for the coming year. The audit schedule typically includes what processes will be audited each month and who the auditors will be.

Receive the report

The management representative receives the audit report to ensure that the audits are thorough and complete, to log in the corrective action requests, and to verify the status of the system.

Monitor/track corrective action

The responsibility for monitoring the status of corrective actions can reside with any appropriate person or persons in the organization. Some organizations leave the monitoring of corrective action to the manager of the area audited. Though this has proven to be effective in some organizations, it has proven to be ineffective in many others.

In the process audit, many findings can be attributed to a breakdown between two or more areas or departments. Which manager will own the corrective action? Will other managers see the finding as a breakdown in "someone else's" area and not actively participate in its resolution? How thorough will the corrective action be if the responsible party is completely responsible for closing it out? In most effective corrective action processes, there is one coordinator who logs the CAR, tracks its status, follows up with appropriate personnel to verify that action has been completed, and arranges for a re-audit of the finding to ensure that corrective action taken was effective. This process is further discussed in Chapters 7 and 8.

Auditee's management

The auditee's management plays a critical role in ensuring the success of the internal audit. Management must demonstrate their support of the audit process and their commitment to using the process as a mechanism to improve the business. Specific roles of the auditee's management are described below.

Approve the selection of the auditors

This can be an emotional issue in discussing audit responsibilities. But the bottom line is that the organization must set itself up to succeed in the audit process.

If the manager sees that an ex-member of the department has been selected as their internal auditor and the auditor left the department due to personnel issues, the manager has a responsibility to raise the issue to ensure the objectivity of the audit. (Reference section 8.2.2 of ISO 9001:2000.) In this case the perception of bias is just as important as whether or not bias actually exists.

Certainly the management team has the authority to approve the selection of the external auditor. If the registrar has had previous experience with a competitor, has previously worked with the organization, or has previously treated the organization's employees with a lack of dignity and respect, management has a right to request that the registration company select another auditor. The same right applies to internal auditing.

Inform employees

To ensure the success of the audit, the auditee's management should notify employees in the department of the upcoming internal audit. The pre-audit meeting with the appropriate personnel might address:

- *What is ISO 9001 and why is it important to this organization?* Why is the organization pursuing or maintaining ISO 9001 registration? Does a major customer require it? Could losing the registration cost the organization a major share of business? If so, employees need to be aware of this. If the audit includes regulatory standards (i.e. FDA mandated GMP requirements, etc.), employees need to understand that major nonconformances in a regulatory audit could close the facility. The internal audit needs to uncover potential noconformances so that they can be addressed prior to a regulatory audit.

  Is the organization pursuing conformance to ISO 9001 as a mechanism to improve the business? If so, employees need to be aware of this. How has ISO 9001 benefited the organization? How has the audit process itself benefited the organization?

- *When will the audit take place?* Though surprise audits may provide a more realistic snapshot of day-to-day operations, nothing will ensure the failure of an internal audit faster than surprising auditees with the audit. Remember that the auditee brings half the knowledge to the table to ensure the audit's success— his/her expertise in the process being reviewed. As such, the audit process needs the active participation of the expert. That participation will be difficult to obtain if the auditee's day was planned and did not include the audit.

- *What will the employees be expected to know?* This is a great time to review the policy statement; its application to the department; the organizational and departmental objectives supporting the policy; how employees impact the organization's ability to meet those objectives; and the current status of the objectives. Employees will also need to know:

  ❑ What documentation is available to employees in the department and how to use that documentation.

  ❑ The activities related to their job.

  ❑ That "I don't know" is the correct answer if they genuinely do not know the answer to the question.

- *How open should the employees be?* During external audits, employees have been correctly advised to answer the question; answer it honestly; answer it thoroughly; then shut up and wait for the next question. Employees need to hear one more time that the internal audit is a different activity with a different purpose. Employees should feel free to raise issues that need to be addressed and use the audit to accomplish its intended purpose—improving the business.

- *What will happen with audit findings?* Who will receive the audit report? Who will be responsible for taking corrective action? How does the corrective action process work?

The odds that managers will adequately cover this information are pretty small without a little help from the management representative. To increase those odds, the management representative should provide a "talk sheet" specifying these questions and answers. The auditor should then verify that the appropriate managers have reviewed this information with their employees prior to the audit.

Provide resources

As discussed earlier, the customer of the internal audit is the area or department being audited. As such, the auditee's management should make every effort to provide the necessary resources to make the audit a success. Necessary resources may include adequate personnel, time to participate in the audit, and access to required records.

Ensure cooperation

Typically, ensuring that employees truly understand the purpose of an internal audit will encourage the employee's cooperation.

Provide guides

Guides are not typically required for internal audits. But if internal auditors are used from sister facilities or if the organization is quite large, the auditor may request a guide to help locate records, find the appropriate offices or audit locations, and ensure that safety regulations are followed where required throughout the facility. If a guide is requested, the area or department being audited should make sure that one is provided.

Guides will almost always be required for external auditors. These guides should be very knowledgeable of the quality management system and be able to locate answers when requested by the auditor. But the guide must not answer questions that have been directed at other employees. They should assist in the audit process only as requested by the auditor.

Provide facilities

Again, the auditee typically provides facilities for external audits and not necessarily for internal audits. If facilities are required during an internal audit, the auditors will usually make arrangements themselves. Facilities required by auditors may include a conference room or quiet office, access to a phone, access to a computer and printer, and an on-site lunch.

Determine corrective action

ISO 9001:2000 clearly states that management of the area audited is responsible for taking corrective action without undue delay. It is neither the auditor's responsibility nor the management representative's responsibility to ensure timely corrective action. The department being audited is much more competent to determine the corrective action that will work best for them.

Should the auditor dictate the appropriate action, the auditee may demonstrate "malicious compliance." The auditee may do exactly as the auditor prescribed knowing the detrimental results that will follow. The auditee can then announce that he/she knew the recommendations would fail, but was told to implement them by the auditor. If the auditor dictates the corrective action, the auditor—not the auditee—will own the results. An objective verification of effectiveness of the corrective action will also be difficult if the auditor specified the actions to be taken.

Ensure corrective action is completed in a timely manner

The management representative is responsible for tracking the corrective action. But it is ultimately the auditee's management that is responsible for taking timely, thorough corrective action following an audit.

Auditor

Of course this entire book describes the responsibilities of internal auditors. But the following will summarize their specific responsibilities.

Thoroughly prepare for the audit

The most important phase of an internal audit is the preparation phase. The methodologies used in preparing for a process-based audit are discussed in Chapter 5. If internal auditors know exactly what records they will be looking at, how many they want to pull and what they will look for when they pull them, their confidence level increases and the quality of the audit is all but ensured.

The phases of audit preparation include:

- Reviewing the standard. The auditor should first review the requirements in ISO 9001:2000 and any other applicable standards relative to the process he/she is auditing to ensure understanding.

- Reviewing available documentation. The auditor should then obtain any available documentation and review it for understanding. The documentation should be compared to the standard to ensure that all requirements have been addressed.

- Preparing a process model for the process being audited. Process models will be discussed further in Chapter 5 and sample process models are provided in Appendix A. To construct a process model, the auditor should first identify the inputs into that process and the desired or expected outputs. Topics for the audit will then include:

❏ Have inputs been clearly defined?

❏ Are employees getting the inputs they need to ensure that desired results are being achieved?

❏ Are responsibilities and authorities clearly defined and understood?

❏ Has the process been clearly established and documented where necessary?

❏ Is the process carried out in accordance with the documentation?

❑ Is the process effective in providing desired or expected results?

• Reviewing previous audit results for trends or other indicators of activities that need special attention.

• Developing a checklist to make certain that the audit verifies the degree to which activities conform to the documented quality management system and the effectiveness of the process in achieving the desired results.

Conduct an opening meeting to initiate the audit

The purpose of the opening meeting is to establish the environment for the audit and ensure that auditors and auditees are on the same page relative to the audit objectives, agenda, and methodologies. The "group opening meeting" is typically held at the beginning of the audit with as many participants as possible. But the most important opening meeting in the internal audit is that held with each individual auditee. These options are described in more detail in Chapter 6.

Gather data to verify conformance to the documented system and the effectiveness of that system

Of course, this is the essence of an internal audit. The auditor should partner with the auditee to evaluate the process and look for opportunities for continual improvement. Tools and techniques for conducting the audit are discussed further in Chapter 6.

Report nonconformities

Nonconformities should be reported right away to give the auditee an opportunity to talk about them. The auditor should take care to avoid emotional terminology that will shut the auditee down. The auditor could simply state, "ISO 9001 requires that we use traceable standards to check the calibration of instruments. Since we don't have those, let me get that down so that we can take care of it before the registrar gets here." That gives the auditee a chance to say, "Oh, I'm sorry. I must have misunderstood your question. The maintenance department keeps those for us. Talk to Bob and see if he doesn't have what you are looking for."

Many auditors have reported invalid findings due to miscommunication. Talking about the finding in clear terms before the end of the conversation provides the opportunity to clear up any miscommunication before the report is issued.

It is also critical that there be no surprises at the closing meeting. To maintain the credibility of the internal audit process, the auditee should know what issues may be brought up in the report before the auditor leaves his/her work area.

Practice appropriate ethics

Internal auditors should adopt an attitude of complete confidentiality with each department that they audit. Using an audit experience in one department as a joke in the next department destroys confidence in the audit process.

Avoid corrective advice

The major pitfalls associated with the auditor prescribing corrective action were discussed earlier in this chapter. But in addition to the auditor owning the problem, recommending corrective advice can shut down the auditee.

When I ask audit class participants to yell out their first thought when I say the word "audit," many participants have responded with, "Someone else coming out here telling me how to do my job." Many employees resent the audit process because they perceive the auditors acting as though they know more about the process being audited than the auditee does. I have heard numerous employees state, "Who does Bob think he is coming out here telling me how I should be doing my job? He has never seen this department in his life and I have been doing this job for 20 years." Recommending resolutions to audit findings can be misinterpreted by the auditee.

When an auditee asks the internal auditor for recommendations, however, most auditors feel that they are obliged to provide the answers. In an internal audit, it may be appropriate to say, "The lab has a pretty good process for controlling their external documents (ASTM procedures). You might want to take a look at their process." Or, "Do you think it would work if you kept your OEM manuals in one place so that folks would know where to find them if they needed them?" In either example, the auditor is making it clear that the auditee is the one who needs to find a way to ensure that their external documents are adequately controlled.

Be able to answer questions

Perhaps the most common question during an internal audit is, "What is ISO 9001 and why are we doing this?" Hopefully this information was covered in an awareness session before the audit, but the auditor should still be ready to answer this question. Other common questions include:

- Will my name be in the audit report?
- What will happen with the findings?
- When will the registrar be here?
- Do I need to fill out this form for ISO 9000?

The auditor should be familiar enough with the internal audit process, the corrective action process, and the ISO 9001 implementation status to be able to answer these questions for the auditees.

Remain within the scope of the audit

In Chapter 6, we will discuss the proper use of a checklist. The checklist is not intended to be a script for the audit that the auditor reads from. Rather it provides a tool to ensure that the basic requirements have been addressed and that evidence has been recorded. The most effective audits are those during which the auditor just talks with the auditee to learn everything they can about the process being audited. If audits are done in pairs, the note-taker is responsible for recording the evidence in the appropriate place while the question-asker is learning everything they can about the process. Using this "conversational" style of auditing will make everyone in the process more comfortable and will uncover more breakdowns in the quality management system than simply reading off a checklist.

Although the advantages of the conversational style of auditing are clear, it can also encourage the auditor to pursue issues that far exceed the original scope of the audit. The auditor may start out auditing the purchasing process and end up in Shipping, out of breath, before the day is over. Exceeding the scope of the audit takes valuable time pursuing issues for which the auditor did not adequately prepare. If the auditor suspects that there may be issues beyond the scope of the audit that need attention, he/she should pass this information along to the management representative or audit coordinator. An additional audit of the other process may be scheduled, if necessary, to pursue the issue.

Issue an audit report within 24 hours of the audit

A common problem in an organization's internal audit process is the lack of timely, thorough corrective action. Though the auditor is not responsible for the corrective action, there are four things that the auditor can do to encourage timely, thorough corrective action. These will be discussed in Chapter 7. One of those items is to issue the report within 24 hours of the audit.

If the report is issued several weeks after an audit, it will typically be filed in the manager's "to be done" pile. The discussion of findings has faded and exactly what the auditor is saying is less clear. The result is that even the most conscientious manager will intend to call the auditor for further clarification. It almost never happens.

The audit report should be issued immediately while discussions are still fresh. Corrective action assignments should be made soon thereafter. The audit reporting process is discussed further in Chapter 7.

Hold a closing meeting
to review audit findings

The audit report should be handed out at the closing meeting. It has been my experience that no closing meeting is equal to no corrective action. The closing meeting is where the manager of the area audited questions each finding for understanding and for validity. The manager should fully understand the finding and why it is a finding by the end of the closing meeting so that he/she can immediately initiate the corrective action.

Now, let's discuss each of the auditor's responsibilities in more detail.

CHAPTER 5

Audit Preparation

Preparing for the internal audit is the most critical phase of the internal audit process. Unless your organization is fortunate enough to have a staff of full time internal auditors, each auditor typically performs only three or four audits a year. To develop the confidence needed to ensure that the process will be thoroughly audited, the auditors must know in advance what evidence they will be looking for, how many records they will need to pull, and what they will be looking for when they pull the records.

If you carefully instructed me on the process of machining a part, I think I could do a pretty good job of machining that part. But if you asked me six months later to machine that part, I doubt that I could produce something that resembled your requirements unless you either gave me some good refresher training or some pretty good job aides. Yet we often ask internal auditors to perform effective audits months after they have received the training without providing adequate tools to ensure their success. This chapter will not only focus on a step-by-step preparation process, but also on providing internal auditors with the necessary tools and techniques to enable effective audits.

An effective audit preparation process includes seven steps:

- Step 1: Define and understand the scope of the audit
- Step 2: Review applicable standards
- Step 3: Review applicable documentation
- Step 4: Prepare a process model
- Step 5: Review previous audit results
- Step 6: Create an effective checklist
- Step 7: Perform a pre-audit meeting

This chapter will discuss each step in the preparation of an internal audit.

Step 1: Define and understand the scope of the audit

Defining the scope of the audit was discussed in Chapter 4. The management representative or audit coordinator is typically responsible for defining the scope of each audit and communicating that scope to the auditors. The audit may cover the entire organization; all processes related to a specific area, department or product; or a specific process within the quality management system. This book will focus primarily on the process-based audit, but the concepts introduced may be applicable to any type of internal audit.

It is the auditors' responsibility to ensure that they understand the scope of the audit before they begin the preparation process. An audit matrix similar to that provided in Appendix D is an excellent tool to communicate which process is being audited and which departments should be included in the audit.

The management representative or audit coordinator can also provide an "audit package" to further clarify what procedures and clauses of ISO 9001:2000 the auditors are responsible for auditing. The audit package typically consists of:

- **Copies of procedures or other documentation to be audited.** Though these procedures must be the current revision, they should not be the "controlled copies" as the auditors will need to highlight them and write on them when they prepare for their audit. These procedures can then be destroyed after the audit or filed with the audit records.

- **A copy of the backbone checklist for the process to be audited.** The auditors will reword this checklist and expand it based on their review of relevant documentation.

- **Results from previous audits.** Auditors need to be aware of previous audit findings so that they can verify the effectiveness of the corrective action that was taken.

Having defined and understood the scope of the audit, the auditor is now ready to review the appropriate clauses of ISO 9001:2000 and other relevant standards.

Step 2: Review applicable standards

Each auditor should perform a careful review of the requirements of each standard against which they will be auditing. Many internal audits are conducted against ISO 9001:2000, but other standards may also apply to an organization. The scope should clearly define the applicable standards as well as the sections of those standards that apply to the audit.

In studying the standard, the auditor may choose to highlight the word "shall" each time it appears. This will allow the auditor to focus on one requirement at a time to ensure that they understand its meaning. It will also facilitate the process of ensuring that processes conform to all requirements of the standard.

If there are requirements that are ambiguous or unclear, the auditor should seek clarification before continuing the preparation process. ISO 9000:2000 is an excellent resource for definitions of terms used in ISO 9001:2000. ISO 9004:2000 is also an excellent source of information for the internal auditor. Although the registrar cannot hold an organization accountable to the contents of ISO 9004:2000, it is an excellent resource to help understand the requirements of ISO 9001:2000. This document is intended to be a guideline to move the organization beyond the basic requirements of ISO 9001. But it is also an excellent tool to understand the process methodology. The management representative or audit coordinator is typically another good resource for clarifying the requirements of ISO 9001.

Step 3: Review applicable documentation

The auditor must also have a good understanding of the organization's documentation that relates to the process being audited. Though not required by ISO 9001:2000, many organizations develop a quality management system that includes three tiers or layers of documentation:

- The quality manual. The quality manual serves as a roadmap to the rest of the system. ISO 9001:2000 requires that the quality manual include:

  ❏ The scope of the quality management system, including any exclusions to ISO 9001:2000 and their justification;

  ❏ The supporting procedures, or a reference to those procedures;

  ❏ A description of the interaction of the processes in the quality management system.

  The manual also typically includes the quality policy and an organization chart or brief description of the organization's structure.

- Procedures. Procedures provide additional information, where required, on the processes in the quality management system. Procedures typically address who will do what and when or how often. There are six documented procedures that are required by ISO 9001:2000:

❑ Control of documents

❑ Control of records

❑ Internal audit

❑ Control of nonconforming product

❑ Corrective action

❑ Preventive action

Beyond these six required procedures, however, ISO 9001:2000 requires "documents needed by the organization to ensure the effective planning, operation, and control of its processes." (Reference 4.2.1.d)

• Work instructions. Work instructions provide more information, where needed, on how specific activities in each process are performed. Work instructions may be in the form of operator instructions, batch sheets, control plans, test methods, calibration instructions, training checklists, audit checklists, raw material specifications, product specifications, drawings, blank forms, etc.

Some organizations will have a fourth tier of documents that include the records. (Reference 4.2.1.e) But records are controlled in an entirely different manner than the rest of the documents. Documents in the first three tiers must be readily available and properly approved and they must be the latest issue with some way to indicate that. (Reference 4.2.3) Records, on the other hand, simply need to be filed in a disciplined manner. (Reference 4.2.4) As such, the auditor should be aware that records are a very different entity in ISO 9001:2000 than other documents and must be handled appropriately.

The auditor should start the document review with a review of the quality manual. The quality manual will "interpret" the requirements of ISO 9001:2000 in the organization's language and should provide some insight into how the standard has been implemented in a specific organization. It should also provide a reference to additional documentation describing the process being studied. The auditor should compare the content of the quality manual to the requirements of ISO 9001:2000 to ensure that the requirements have been adequately addressed.

The next step in the document review process is to read, study and understand any second tier procedures that may be available for the process being audited. In reading these documents, the auditor may choose to highlight those items that will help create an effective checklist:

- *Flags.* These are requirements in the procedure that make you say, "When donkeys fly." In a new quality management system, flags are created when authors of the procedures start with what they think the process should look like some day versus what it looks like today. In a mature system, flags are created when processes are changed, but documentation has not been updated to reflect that change. Though not always, flags typically indicate that the procedure should be updated to reflect actual practice.

Some common flags from the author's perspective include:

❑ "All corrective actions will be closed out in 30 days."

❑ "All supplier corrective actions are due back in the Purchasing office within three business days."

❑ "The following seventeen signatures are required on each quality procedure."

❑ "All eight of the following managers are required to attend each monthly management review meeting."

• *Points to verify.* These are requirements that are not flags, but that the auditor would be interested in verifying during the audit. Examples may include:

❑ "The management representative issues an annual internal audit schedule. The schedule ensures that each process in the quality management system and each area in the company are audited every year."

❑ "Internal auditors must receive training on the requirements of ISO 9001:2000 and audit techniques. They must then complete two audits with a qualified auditor before being qualified themselves."

❑ "The QA Technician samples the product every four hours and performs the following inspections. . . ."

❑ "The Quality Manager conducts customer focus groups monthly and forwards results to the Management Representative. The Management Representative analyzes the results and initiates corrective or preventive actions as necessary."

- *Responsibilities and authorities.* From a technical standpoint, the auditor should make note of responsibilities and authorities to ensure that they have been defined as required in section 5.5.1 of ISO 9001:2000. Of course, ISO 9001 does not dictate that these be documented in procedures, but they most often are. If the auditor reads the procedure and does not know who is responsible for performing each activity, this may be a flag. The auditor should verify during the audit that responsibilities and authorities have indeed been well defined and communicated.

From a practical standpoint, the auditor should highlight responsibilities and authorities so that he/she will know with whom to talk during the audit. If the responsible position is noted beside each section of questions on the audit checklist, time is saved during the audit that would otherwise be spent chasing down the right people.

- *Records.* Finally, the auditor should highlight the names of records so that they can begin learning the language of the auditee. Asking operators where they record their "quality critical process parameters" is not speaking the correct language. After a good document review, the auditor will know to ask for the "daily log sheet," "DCS parameters," "operator's log sheet," or other terminology that the auditee uses. The audit progresses more smoothly for both parties when the auditor knows the language of the auditee.

The content of any available procedures should be compared to the requirements of ISO 9001 to verify that the process meets specified requirements.

Depending on the process being audited, the auditor may pull some of the third tier work instructions or blank forms to understand the process and the type of documentation that supports the process. The majority of audit preparation, however, is typically spent studying any available second tier procedures.

If the process being audited is very new to the auditor, the internal auditor may request a pre-audit tour of the area. Other trained auditors who work in that area are typically happy to show the auditor around and briefly explain the process. A pre-audit tour may be quite helpful in understanding the procedures and the process.

Step 4: Prepare a process model

When the auditor understands the requirements of the standard as well as the requirements of the organization's documentation, a process model should then be prepared.

To prepare a process model, first identify those inputs that feed into the process being audited. These typically represent interfaces with other processes in the organization. Examples of inputs into a manufacturing process, for example, might include:

- Raw materials that arrive on time and meet the organization's specifications
- Well maintained process equipment
- Accurate instrumentation
- Controlled instructions, batch sheets, prints, and other documentation
- Product specifications
- Production schedule
- Identification / traceability requirements
- Handling and storage requirements
- Packaging and shipping requirements
- Organizational / departmental objectives
- Qualified, competent personnel

Then identify the desired or expected results of the process. The desired or expected results of a manufacturing process, for example, would be acceptable product produced on time at a competitive cost (i.e.: minimal scrap or rework). Other outputs of a manufacturing process will include process control records that provide evidence of conformance to quality management system requirements.

Sample process models for the following processes have been provided in Appendix A of this book.

- Quality planning
- Management review
- Competence, awareness and training
- Maintenance
- Planning for product realization
- Customer-related processes
- Design and development control
- Purchasing
- Product or service realization
- Control of monitoring and measuring equipment
- Customer satisfaction
- Internal quality audit
- Monitoring and measurement of product
- Control of nonconforming product
- Corrective action
- Preventive action

These process models have also been provided on a CD so that they can be easily customized to fit your organization. These models are generic in nature and must be revised as necessary to fit the specific components of an organization's quality management system. Once defined for your organization, they may be used as audit tools for future audit teams.

The effectiveness of the process can then be evaluated using the process model as a starting point.

- *Have required inputs been clearly defined?*

  A common reason that process inputs are not adequate to ensure the effective implementation of the process is that the input requirements have simply never been clearly defined.

  The lack of well-defined input requirements is a common source of findings that can generate return on investment. In one of several examples where I found that Purchasing was not receiving production schedules in time to meet suppliers' lead times, I discovered the cause of the problem to be the lack of clearly communicated needs and expectations of the buyer in Purchasing. The Production Scheduler had the ability to get an estimated schedule to the buyer several weeks in advance. He simply did not know the buyer needed it then. This finding led to cost savings related to premium freight, lost production time, and unnecessary product changeovers.

  An input of the training process is well-defined competency requirements for a position. Training may be lacking in an area because competency requirements have not been defined. A new employee is left to learn through their mistakes. Depending on the position, these mistakes can be quite costly. Poorly defined training needs in Maintenance can lead to excessive downtime and higher costs related to spare parts, scrap, and rework. Poorly defined training needs in sales can lead to orders being accepted that manufacturing or servicing simply cannot meet, poorly defined customer requirements and dissatisfied customers. The ultimate results are excessive production costs, more premium freight, and lost business.

* *Are employees getting the inputs they need to ensure that desired results can be achieved?*

Even when input requirements are well defined, the inputs may not be adequate to meet the needs of the auditee.

Examples of process inputs not meeting the needs of the user might include:

❑ Prints and specifications with tolerances that are illegible or cannot be met by the current manufacturing process;

❑ Schedules that cannot be met by production;

❑ Training requirements that focus primarily on human resource issues (i.e.: how to schedule vacation time, how to call in sick, etc.) and omit job-specific training issues;

❑ Equipment with a history of excessive downtime;

❑ Software programs that are cumbersome, difficult to understand, and do not meet the needs of the user;

❑ Poorly calibrated instrumentation;

❑ Inadequately defined customer requirements;

❑ Poorly designed customer satisfaction survey results that do not provide adequate information to initiate corrective or preventive actions.

These are all examples of interfaces between processes that have broken down. Where these problems exist, corrective action will typically involve a team of employees representing the applicable processes to resolve the problem. Internal audits can be used as the motivation to address these issues and effectively resolve them.

- *Are responsibilities and authorities clearly defined and understood?*

  The lack of clearly defined responsibilities and authorities is at the root of about a fourth to a third of the findings in the audits that I perform. As organizations strive to streamline and simplify their documented processes, the first things that disappear from the procedures are the defined responsibilities and authorities. As organizations restructure and reorganize, clear responsibilities and authorities may not be adequately defined for the new positions.

  The auditor should verify that responsibilities and authorities are clearly spelled out in any available documentation. As we discussed earlier, if they are not defined in documents provided for review, there may be a flag for the auditor to explore. During the audit, the auditor should verify that responsibilities and authorities are clearly understood as described in the documentation.

Examples of responsibilities and authorities that may not be clearly understood include:

❑ Who follows up on supplier corrective action when the supplier does not respond?

❑ Who compares receiving inspection results to established specifications when a shipment arrives?

❑ Who verifies the effectiveness of corrective actions?

❑ Who monitors websites for potential inquiries from customers?

❑ Who receives production/service data and what action is expected based on the data?

❑ Who tracks action items following a management review?

- *Has the process been clearly established and documented where necessary?*

ISO 9001:2000 takes some emphasis off documentation requirements by specifying only six required procedures:

❑ Control of documents

❑ Control of records

❑ Internal audits

❑ Control of nonconforming product

❑ Corrective action

❑ Preventive action

But requirement 4.2.1.d goes on to say that the organization must have additional documentation as required to control the processes within its quality management system. Where skills can be taught and verified during the training process, documentation on how to perform that skill is rarely needed. Examples may include reading a micrometer, measuring the length of the product using a tape measure, or reading a print.

Where minimum requirements for a position require some basic certification or degree, the skills that should have been mastered during the certification process do not typically need to be documented. But often documentation is needed to train these employees on the processes and equipment that are specific to your organization. For example:

❑ A certified welder would probably not need instructions on general welding techniques, but may need instructions on issues that are specific to your products or equipment.

❑ A registered nurse (RN) may not need a detailed instruction on how to give a shot, but may need a documented instruction on how to operate the autoclave equipment at your facility.

❑ A Professional Engineer (PE) would not need documented instructions on basic engineering concepts, but would typically need documentation describing the print control process or the project management requirements at your organization.

In assessing whether or not adequate documentation exists, the new employee can be a valuable resource. The primary customer of documented procedures is typically the new employee. This customer is then in the best position to evaluate the effectiveness of that documentation. The auditor may ask questions like:

❑ Were you trained by the procedures/instructions in this department?

❑ If so, were they helpful to you?

❑ If not, why not? Were they too long? Too short? Non-existent? Incorrect?

This information is invaluable in assessing the adequacy of documentation for that process.

- *Is the process carried out in accordance with the documentation?*

This is the compliance auditing with which we are most familiar. As the auditor reviewed available documentation, he/she should have highlighted those items that warranted verification during the audit. As such, the audit will verify conformance to the documented quality management system as well as to the standard itself. In preparing for the audit, auditors should identify what records they will need to pull to verify conformance to the documentation, how many they will want to pull and what they will be looking for when they pull the records.

- *Is the process effective in providing desired or expected results?*

   Are any metrics being maintained which would indicate the effectiveness of the process? For a manufacturing process, these may include productivity, on-time delivery, first pass rate, scrap rate, rework, etc. For a purchasing process, these may include on-time arrival of purchased parts and materials, reject rate at receiving, etc. Examples of potential metrics are provided for each process in Appendix A. These metrics can be evaluated to determine the effectiveness of the process in achieving the desired or expected results of the process. If these metrics are not being maintained, the auditor must evaluate how the effectiveness can be determined.

Understanding the process model for the process being audited is critical in evaluating the effectiveness of that process.

Once thorough process models have been developed, future auditors can use them in their audit preparation. "Prepare a process model" then becomes "review the process model," saving a significant amount of time in the preparation process.

Step 5: Review previous audit results

The auditor should complete the document review process by reviewing the results of previous internal and external audits. The effectiveness of action taken for previous findings can then be evaluated. Repetitive audit findings in a given area may be an indicator that the auditor should focus on that area until the issues have been fully resolved.

Step 6: Create an effective checklist

Perhaps the hottest debate in conducting effective internal audits is whether or not the auditor should be given a pre-developed checklist of basic questions to use as a guide in the audit process. I believe that we need to provide the tools that are necessary for successful audits and that an effective checklist is one of those tools.

As I mentioned earlier in the book, if you thoroughly trained me on how to perform a specific task, I could probably meet your requirements that day. But if you ask me to perform that task for the first time six months later, I seriously doubt that I would be capable of doing an adequate job. Yet we often put our internal auditors in this position.

Unless your organization is fortunate enough to have full time auditors, your internal auditors may conduct as many as two to four audits a year. These auditors are often asked to squeeze effective auditing into their already loaded list of responsibilities and to perform these audits as long as three to six months after the training was provided. In doing so, we set up our auditors to fail in their attempt to perform thorough audits that reveal specific opportunities to improve the business and result in tangible returns to the bottom line.

Rather than withholding the tools that auditors need to be successful, I believe we need to provide those tools and find ways to make them useful in achieving the desired results. Checklists can be designed to fully evaluate conformance to specified standards and documentation and also evaluate the effectiveness of audited processes. But regardless of the checklist design, auditors must remember that checklists are intended to serve as guidelines for the audit and not scripts. The effective use of a checklist is further discussed in Chapter 6.

A "backbone" checklist is a list of questions and/or evidence that needs to be included in the audit to verify conformance to ISO 9001:2000 and to the basic requirements of the organization's documented quality management system. An example of a template for such a checklist is given in Appendix B of this book and also provided on a CD to facilitate its customization. This checklist is NOT intended to be used as it is written. It must be customized to include your organization's terminology and requirements. But it provides a solid basis on which to build.

At first glance, the checklist in Appendix B can be quite intimidating. But most internal audits include only one of the many processes covered in this comprehensive checklist. An audit of an individual process may only involve four or five pages.

There are several advantages to using a well-designed "backbone" checklist during the internal audit. Those advantages are discussed below.

Pre-designed "backbone" checklists improve consistency among the auditors. A common complaint of any type of audit is that the results depend more on who the auditor was than on the health of the process. But if all auditors are using the same "backbone" checklist, the results will more accurately reflect the effectiveness of the process being audited. Consider, for example, the following question on a checklist.

Pull 10 Corrective Action Requests at random and verify the following:

- Was the cause of the problem identified and recorded on the CAR?

- Was action taken which should have eliminated the cause?

- Is there evidence that the action taken was effective?

- Were any associated documents updated as a result of the action taken? (Pull any documents that should have been updated and verify that they have indeed been issued and that affected employees are aware of the change.)

If every auditor used this question as a starting point to verify conformance to the standard and to the organization's own documented procedure, the results of an audit of corrective action would be somewhat consistent. Of course further questions would be necessary to fully verify conformance to ISO 9001:2000 and to verify the effectiveness of the process. See Appendix B for additional sample questions for corrective action.

A well-designed "backbone" checklist ensures thorough coverage of the quality management system. As I audit quality management systems, a common problem that I see is that audits do not thoroughly cover the requirements of ISO 9001:2000. If internal auditors are left on their own to create an audit plan from scratch before every audit, the audits get more and more shallow as time constraints become tighter and tighter. The end result is often two or three questions that address a given process. A ten-minute audit of any process is not typically sufficient to fully verify conformance and effectiveness.

Using a good "backbone" checklist, however, enables the auditors to make sure that the process is effectively meeting the basic requirements of ISO 9001:2000 and the organization's documented quality management system.

A well-designed "backbone" checklist also provides plenty of space for recording facts and data observed during the audit. A common finding on registration audits is that there is plenty of evidence to support the negative issues found during an audit, but little evidence of processes that were found to be in good shape. A well-designed "backbone" checklist provides space to record evidence of the good as well as evidence of the bad. The auditor has not completed the audit until there is evidence recorded for each applicable question.

But the biggest benefit of a "backbone" checklist is that it saves a significant amount of time in preparing for the audit. Internal auditors often tell me that it is tough to find time to adequately prepare for the audit. As we have discussed, internal auditors are required to read and study the applicable sections of ISO 9001:2000; to read and study applicable procedures or other documentation; to review past internal audit findings and to create an effective audit plan. These are difficult tasks to fit into an already overloaded schedule. Anything we can do to make the internal auditor's job easier and more effective is appreciated by everyone.

But I certainly acknowledge the concerns of many that audit checklists are detrimental to the audit process. The most common reasons that I hear for not providing "backbone" checklists for the auditors is that they cause audits to become stale and discourage adequate preparation.

"Backbone" checklists may cause audits to become stale. This is a common complaint when the checklist is based on "yes/no" questions or questions that do not require the review of specific records. Most checklists available for purchase can be thoroughly completed without pulling a single record. The really poor checklists are based on "yes/no" questions and even have only a place to check "complies" or "does not comply" without space to record the specific evidence that was observed during the audit. Examples of such questions include:

- Do you have a corrective action procedure?

- Does it address the identification of the cause of the problem?

- Does it address removing the cause of the problem?

- Does it require that actions taken must be evaluated for effectiveness before they are closed out?

These questions are great for a system audit to verify conformance of the procedures to ISO 9001:2000, but are inadequate to determine whether or not activities actually conform to the requirements.

Better checklists have questions like:

- What processes are used to determine the causes of problems?

- Who is responsible for ensuring that actions are taken to eliminate the causes?

- How do you determine whether or not actions taken have been effective?

- What process do you have in place to ensure that any associated documentation is updated based on the actions taken?

These are terrific questions to ask to ensure that processes are in place, but again, do not verify that processes conform to ISO 9001:2000 nor do they verify that processes are effective. Both of these checklists will lead to stale audits over the years if the auditors simply read off the checklists. At some point the auditee will respond with, "Don't waste your breath. The answer to question one is in this pile; the answer to number two is in this pile. . . ."

To overcome the stale audit, we must prepare checklists that are based on facts and data. Really good conformance checklists will identify what evidence is to be reviewed, how many samples should be pulled, and what the auditor should look for when they pull them. Asking the four questions above can be effective as long as they are followed with:

"Pull 10 Corrective Action Requests at random and verify the following:

- Was the cause of the problem identified and recorded on the CAR?

- Was action taken which should have eliminated the cause?

- Is there evidence that the action taken was effective?

- Were any associated documents updated as a result of the action taken? (Pull any documents that should have been updated and verify that they have indeed been issued and that affected employees are aware of the change.)"

These questions will not allow the audit process to become stale as different records will be pulled each year to verify that the corrective action process is in conformance with specified requirements. Then the auditor will use the process model to formulate questions to verify the effectiveness of the process. The full process for developing effective checklists is described below.

Using a "backbone" checklist discourages adequate preparation. I agree with this argument. At some point during the life of the audit process, the "backbone" checklist will become really good. It will be tempting for the auditor to go out and just use this checklist to do their audit. And, indeed, they will do a decent audit. But to completely verify the effectiveness of the process being audited, the auditor will need to follow each of the preparation steps outlined above. When the "backbone" checklist has evolved into a highly effective internal audit tool, the management representative or audit coordinator should follow up with each auditor before the audit to see what types of things they highlighted during their document review and what questions they added to their "backbone" checklist. Doing so will ensure that the auditors have adequately prepared for their audit. It is difficult to audit against a procedure that you have never read.

So what is the ultimate resolution? Again, I recommend that a "backbone" checklist be provided to the internal auditor, but that the following rules be used with it:

- Checklists should be based on facts and data and not "yes/no" questions or only open-ended questions.

- Checklists should be used by the auditor as a guideline to the audit and not a script. The checklist should not be read to the auditee. See Chapter 6 for a further discussion on the effective use of a checklist during the actual audit.

How do you develop an effective "backbone" checklist?

This is the million-dollar question. A good audit checklist is the most valuable tool your organization can develop to encourage successful internal audits.

The first audit team for each process can help develop the first round of "backbone" checklists. The checklists will then be refined with each subsequent audit. After three or four rounds of audits, the "backbone" checklist becomes a powerful tool in verifying conformance of the process to specified requirements and the effectiveness of the process in achieving the desired results.

After completing a thorough document review, the first step in developing a good "backbone" checklist is to reword a standard audit checklist to incorporate your organization's specific terminology. An example of a standard audit checklist is provided in Appendix B. It is also provided on a CD to facilitate this process.

The checklist provided in Appendix B uses a combination of questions and audit matrices to define the requirements to be reviewed in the audit. Each process begins with a broad, open question to get the auditee talking to the auditor. Audit matrices are used when records are being pulled to provide the auditor an opportunity to easily record the evidence that was observed. The matrix also provides instruction on what record to pull and what to look for when the record is pulled. Each process then ends with an open question or questions to evaluate the effectiveness of that process.

Using matrices to record audit results saves significant time in the audit process and ensures that adequate records of audit activities are maintained. The matrices will identify what records are to be pulled and what information should be verified when the records are pulled. Some cells in the audit matrix are split. (Reference Section 4.2.3 in Appendix B for the document control matrix.) The top half of the split cells may be completed during the preparation process to indicate what the procedure requires for that item. In the document control matrix, for example, the approval column contains split cells. The auditors can record in the top half who has the authority to approve each document. In doing so, the auditor has all the information he/she needs without having to fumble through procedures during the audit. The results of the audit can then be recorded in the bottom half of the cell (i.e., how many of the documents observed during the audit were approved by the correct person).

When starting with any generic audit checklist, it is recommended that you follow the steps below to ensure that it adequately represents your specific organization and its quality management system:

Reword each question on the checklist to incorporate your organization's specific terminology

Using a generic checklist without customizing it to reflect the terminology and practices of a specific organization is a mistake that will inevitably lead to unsuccessful audits. The auditees—and even the auditors—often do not understand the questions in the checklist or the types of records that need to be evaluated.

The number of records to be pulled must also be customized to meet the needs of the organization. There is no requirement for minimum sample sizes, but the general rule of thumb for management system audits is three to ten with a lot of common sense. Common sense should consider:

- How many samples there are to choose from and
- How long it will take to audit a single sample.

If your organization performs annual management reviews, for example, auditing three management review meeting minutes would be a bit excessive. The appropriate sample size in this situation would be one. If you were going to audit the complete traceability of an airplane wing, three would again be a bit excessive due to the time it would take to complete a thorough audit of one sample.

If the record being pulled is the primary record for the entire audit, the auditor will probably want to pull ten samples. Corrective Action Requests (CARs), for example, will be the primary record that will be evaluated in an audit of the corrective action process. Auditing ten CARs would not be unreasonable.

Minimal sample sizes should be determined during the checklist development phase. As the audit is conducted, the auditor may decide to increase the sample size if necessary to determine the extent of a finding.

In order to practice rewording a generic checklist to fit the unique terminology of an organization, please review the training procedure that has been provided in Appendix C of this book. A typical Job Description and Training Checklist for a laboratory technician follow the procedure to give the reader a better understanding of this organization's training process.

You may choose to print these documents from the enclosed CD to have them in front of you as we customize Section 6.2 of the generic checklist for the specific training process at Acme.

The first two questions in Section 6.2 of the checklist in Appendix B are probably adequate in the way that they are stated. But the columns on the training records matrix should be customized to fit this specific process.

Competency requirements for Acme are defined on the Job Description and associated Training Checklist for each position. So the second column can be changed from "Are competency requirements defined?" to "Is there a current Job Description and Training Checklist for this position?" A second column can be added to ask, "Do the Job Description and Training Checklist adequately define competency requirements for this position?" Though these column headings ask questions that can be easily answered with either "yes" or "no," the completed matrix will result in findings based on facts and data, i.e.:

- Two of five positions audited did not have associated training checklists.

- Job descriptions did not exist for three of the five positions audited.

At Acme, the evidence that new employee training requirements have been met is the completion of the Training Checklist. So the column currently reading "Was required training provided?" can be changed to "Was the training checklist thoroughly completed?"

The effectiveness of new employee training at Acme is evaluated in two ways. The first method involves the supervisor or manager reviewing information with the new employee. The evidence of that review is the appropriate signature on the Training Checklist. Because there is a space for this signature on the Training Checklist, verification of the completion of this requirement has already been addressed.

The second method of training evaluation is to have the new employee complete a New Employee Training Evaluation form. The column that reads, "Was effectiveness of training evaluated?" can be changed to "Did the new employee complete a New Employee Training Evaluation Form?" The final column can remain as it is worded.

In question 3, the word "trainer" can be changed to "sponsor" to match the terminology of Acme.

Question 4 can be reworded now to add specific details on how training needs are assessed for experienced employees. It can be replaced with the following two questions.

- "Pull management review meeting minutes and verify that plant-wide training needs have been assessed during the previous year. Pull records to verify that identified training needs have been planned for or provided."

- "Pull assessed training needs for five experienced employees at random. Pull records to verify that identified training needs have been planned for or provided."

Add questions to the checklist from the document review

Having highlighted those requirements in the procedures that you thought warranted verification will facilitate this process. If the checklist does not already incorporate the highlighted items, add questions in the appropriate places to address those issues.

In the Acme procedure, for example, there are several items in the procedure that are not already covered on the checklist. One item might be a review of the New Employee Training Evaluation Forms to look for any trends or significant comments that may provide for opportunities to improve the training process. A question might be added to the checklist that reads:

- How are New Employee Training Forms evaluated to identify opportunities to improve the training process? (Review the forms for any trends or significant comments that may indicate an opportunity for improvement. Verify that indicated action has indeed been taken.)

There may be a number of other issues that auditors would like to verify during the audit. These questions should be added to the customized "backbone" checklist before each audit. These additional questions, which do not appear on the standard checklist, will help keep the audit process fresh over the years.

Review the process model and ensure that the checklist adequately addresses whether or not inputs are adequate to achieve desired results

An example of a process model for the training process is provided in Appendix A of this book. The general inputs are identified as:

- Defined competence requirements; (Addressed in the training record matrix)

- Defined individual training needs; (Addressed in the training record matrix)

- Defined organizational training needs; (Addressed in the review of management review meeting minutes)

- Qualified trainers (or sponsors/mentors); (Addressed in question 3)

- Adequate procedures; (Addressed in question 7)

- Adequate work instructions; (Addressed in question 7)

- Career planning needs; (Addressed in questions 4 and 5)

- Training evaluation criteria; (Addressed in question 6)

- Applicable organizational or departmental objectives; (Addressed in the training record matrix)

Each of the inputs has already been addressed in the current checklist. If the adequacy of any input requirements were not already covered, the auditor should add additional questions to ensure that all inputs have been well defined and are being provided in a way that meets the needs of those employees working in the process.

Again, review the process model and determine how to verify that the desired outputs are being achieved

The desired results of a training process are qualified and competent personnel. Potential methods to evaluate the effectiveness of the training process are identified at the bottom of the process model in Appendix A. But perhaps the best method is to interview the customer of the training process—the new employee. He or she is typically in the best position to evaluate the effectiveness of the process. Some good questions to ask to evaluate the effectiveness of training might include:

- Were you trained by the procedures or work instructions in this department?

- If so, were they helpful to you?

- If not, why not? Were they too long? Too short? Nonexistent? Incorrect? Obsolete?

- What have you learned since you have been at this organization that you wish had been included in the training process?

- Please rate our training process on a scale of 1-10. If you rated it less than 7, what specific opportunities for improvement would you recommend?

Any significant comments from these questions should be listed as observations in the audit report.

Based on these steps, the new "backbone" checklist for Acme's training process is included at the end of Appendix C.

This training checklist needed some extensive customization to make it fit the terminology and requirements of Acme manufacturing. You will find that some sections will need more customization than others. Document control, management review, design and development control, internal audits, and corrective action, for example, will typically need minimal alteration. But defining and reviewing customer requirements, purchasing, and process control will typically need more extensive customization. It is critical that the "backbone" checklist you develop include the specific terminology and requirements of your organization if your internal audits are to be effective.

The preceding discussion on creating an effective internal audit checklist primarily focused on the first round of internal audits. Once an effective "backbone" checklist has been established, this step becomes, "Review the 'backbone' checklist for understanding. Reword any questions that need clarification. Add questions to the checklist from your highlighted procedures." This will save significant time in audit preparation.

Step 7: Conduct a pre-audit meeting

Just prior to the audit, the supervisor or manager of the primary area being audited should review with their employees information that is critical to the audit. As previously discussed in Chapter 4, employees need to know:

- What is ISO 9001:2000 and why is it important to our organization? Be specific. Do customers require registration for future business? Does the organization see the quality management system as a means to improve the business? If so, what successes have already been experienced? If return on investment has been calculated for previous audit results, this should be shared with the employees.

- When will the audit take place? What will be the audit agenda?

- What will employees be expected to know? Employees need to know that they will be expected to understand the quality policy and objectives and understand how their activities impact the organization's ability to meet those objectives. This is a great opportunity to review what those objectives are and provide employees a review of the organization's status toward meeting those objectives. Employees will also need to know where their documentation is located and how to use that documentation. Finally, they simply need to know their jobs. Employees need to understand that "I do not know" is an acceptable response in an audit. The auditor may simply be asking the wrong person.

- How open should employees be during the audit? For internal audits, this is a great opportunity to remind employees that they are the customers of the audit process. If there are processes that are not working correctly in their area, having them recorded in the audit report may be the incentive that brings appropriate attention to the problem. Of course, if this briefing is provided prior to an external audit, employees should be advised to "answer the question honestly and thoroughly, then shut up and wait for the next question."

This information can be reviewed in departmental meetings, department announcements, via e-mail or even on a communication board. To encourage the supervisor or manager to cover this information, the management representative or audit coordinator may provide a talk sheet with preprinted questions and answers.

Summary of audit preparation

To summarize the audit preparation phase, let's review the specific steps to be followed in preparing for the FIRST audit of a specific process.

- Step 1: Define and understand the scope of the audit.
    - ❑ What sections of ISO 9001:2000 should be covered in the audit?
    - ❑ What procedures or other documentation is applicable to this process?
    - ❑ What areas of the organization will the auditor need to include to ensure that the audit scope is thoroughly covered?

- Step 2: Read, study and understand the applicable sections of ISO 9001:2000.

- Step 3: Read, study and understand applicable documentation.
    - ❑ Compare to the standard for conformance.
    - ❑ Highlight those items that you would like to verify during the audit. These may include flags, points to verify, responsibilities, and the names of records.

- Step 4: Develop a process model.

  ❑ Identify the inputs into the process.

  ❑ Identify the desired results or outputs of the process.

- Step 5: Review previous audit results.

- Step 6: Create an effective "backbone" checklist.

  ❑ Start with the checklist provided in Appendix B.

  ❑ Reword each question on the checklist to incorporate your organization's specific terminology.

  ❑ Add questions to the checklist from the document review and review of previous audits.

  ❑ Review the process model and ensure that the checklist adequately addresses whether or not inputs are adequate to achieve desired results.

  ❑ Again, review the process model and determine how to verify that the desired outputs are being achieved.

- Step 7: Conduct a pre-audit meeting.

The preparation phase in subsequent audits of each process will be similar, but much less time-consuming.

- Step 1: Define and understand the scope of the audit.

  ❑ What sections of ISO 9001:2000 should be covered in the audit?

❑ What procedures or other documentation is applicable to this process?

❑ What areas of the organization will the auditor need to visit to ensure that the audit scope is thoroughly covered?

- Step 2: Read, study and understand the applicable sections of ISO 9001:2000.

- Step 3: Read, study and understand applicable documentation.

  ❑ Compare to the standard for conformance.

  ❑ Highlight those items that you would like to verify during the audit. These may include flags, points to verify, responsibilities and the names of records.

- Step 4: Review the applicable process model for understanding.

- Step 5: Review previous audit results.

- Step 6: Review the "backbone" checklist for understanding.

  ❑ Reword any questions that need clarification.

  ❑ Add questions to the checklist from your highlighted procedures.

- Step 7: Conduct a pre-audit meeting.

Using this disciplined approach to audit preparation will increase the confidence level of the internal auditor and all but ensure the success of the audit.

CHAPTER *6*

Performing the Audit

The critical stage of an effective internal audit has already been completed. If the auditors have thoroughly prepared for the audit, they should know what records they will be pulling, how many they will pull, and what they will look for when they pull them. In addition, they should have developed a strategy to evaluate the effectiveness of the process being audited. Conducting the audit then becomes an exercise of completing the audit plan while treating the auditees with dignity and respect.

The "group" opening meeting

Each audit should begin with a brief opening meeting with as many of the auditees present as possible. The purpose of the opening meeting is to establish the environment of the audit. The lead auditor should chair the opening meeting, which typically includes the following agenda:

- The purpose of the audit
- The audit plan
- The time and location of the closing meeting
- Questions from the auditees

For an internal audit, the "group" opening meeting can be as formal or as informal as is appropriate for the size and culture of the organization. For small organizations where employees know each other well, the opening meeting may simply be a five-minute gathering in the department to make sure everyone is aware of the audit, its purpose, and its agenda. In a large organization or in organizations where internal auditors are used from other site locations, the opening meeting should be a more formal event—typically conducted in a conference room or meeting area. Regardless of the formality, the opening meeting should not take more than 15–20 minutes.

The "individual" opening meeting

In the internal audit, the "individual" opening meeting is the more critical of the two. If the auditor approaches an auditee and immediately begins asking questions related to the audit, the auditee typically will not know the answer to the first several questions. Their mind was probably on something else when the auditor approached them. They need just a moment to transition to the audit. This is an excellent time to ensure one-on-one that the auditee is comfortable with the purpose of the audit.

Clearly restate the purpose of the audit and invite questions from the auditee

If the auditee feels that ISO 9001 is just a pile of useless paperwork, then give them a chance to express that feeling. From a personal standpoint, my heart leaps out of my chest when an angry auditee belts that out. I know that I am about to pull the auditee onto the audit team. And that is my goal. I cannot complete an effective audit without his or her expertise on the process.

In helping a client with a recent internal audit, I introduced myself to the auditee, explained the purpose of the audit, and asked if he had any questions about ISO 9001:2000 or the audit process. He angrily replied that ISO 9001:2000 was the most useless pile of junk he had ever experienced on the job. (This is the printable translation of his comments.) Furthermore, it was actually costing him money out of his own wallet!

Operations personnel are paid at this facility based on quotas. If you exceed the quota for your position, you make bonus pay. Before the implementation of the ISO 9001 requirements, this operator had made a significant bonus in each paycheck. But since the requirements had been fully implemented, he often failed to even meet his quota.

Having helped companies implement the requirements of ISO 9001 for over thirteen years, I am fully aware of an organization's tendency to over-document their system. This situation is only one of the detrimental effects of an over-documented process. When I hear such an emotional response to ISO 9001, I know that we have an opportunity through this audit to simplify the process being audited, create a believer in the internal audit process, and make the organization a lot of money in increased productivity.

After explaining that it was never the intent of ISO 9001:2000 to decrease productivity and to frustrate the workforce with worthless paperwork, I asked the auditee for his help in explaining where the organization might have gotten a little "overly enthusiastic" in implementing the requirements of ISO 9001. Suddenly I had seventeen assistant auditors. Each operator joyfully joined the audit process, bringing to me the forms they had to complete on a daily basis and showing me numerous examples where the same information was being recorded in two, three, or more different places. As a result of the audit, we were able to take the 27 *forms* required in this simple manufacturing process and turn them into two forms—one on the front end of the line and one on the back end.

The bottom line in this organization is that process and quality engineers still receive the information they need to reduce quality failures and to increase productivity, but the method was optimized so that operations personnel could see the value and participate in the improvement process. Everyone came out of the audit a winner. Though this organization does not calculate return on investment for their audit findings, I suspect the increased productivity as a result of this audit generated at least six figures on the bottom line.

Though the quantity of paperwork in this example was a bit unusual, having the auditee express their frustration with the process and using the audit to deal with those frustrations, if possible, is not unusual at all. If the auditee is given an opportunity at the beginning of the audit to ask questions about the management system and the audit process, the internal auditor may learn critical information on how that audit can be used to improve the business. Again, the auditee is the expert on their process and typically knows where the opportunities for improvement lie. Give them a chance to tell you.

Invite the auditee to read the notes taken during the audit and correct any errors

When I write the word "audit" on a flipchart pad at the beginning of my internal audit classes and ask participants to yell out their first thought, I often hear comments like, "IRS!" "Pink slip!" "Vacation day!" "Fear!" and "Somebody else coming out here telling me how to do my job!" But several years ago, one gentleman yelled out "Clipboard!" That insight spoke volumes to me. Staring at the backside of an auditor's clipboard as copious notes are being taken is probably the most intimidating, disrespectful aspect of most audits.

If two auditors are used, the note-taker should sit or stand in such a way that the auditee can easily read the notes that are being taken. The auditors should then explain that these notes belong to the entire audit team—including the auditee. The auditee should be invited to read the notes and bring anything to the attention of the auditors that is incorrect or was misunderstood.

I learned this lesson early in my audit career. During my very first audit as a Supplier Engineer with 3M, I asked a Lab Technician, "Do you calibrate your instruments?" The Lab Technician said, "No." Hot dog! I had found my first major finding! I dutifully recorded on the checklist clutched to my chest that the organization had no calibration process.

Let's count how many things are wrong with this picture. This was not one of my more intelligent opening questions. I had intended to ask whether or not the organization had a calibration process. But because I did not word the question correctly, the Technician assumed I was asking if HE calibrated the instruments. Furthermore, the first question should be a broad, open question to get the auditee talking to you. I should have asked, "Please explain the calibration process here at XYZ Company." I would have learned a lot more about the process.

But had I allowed the auditee to read my notes—and even invited him to do so—I would have avoided that embarrassing moment at the closing meeting when I announced to management that the organization had no calibration process. The managers looked at each other with confused expressions and replied, "We have a very reputable company down the street calibrate our instruments once a month. Is that not acceptable to you?" OUCH.

Inviting the auditee to read the audit notes not only shows respect for the expertise of the auditee, but will also prevent many incorrect audit findings.

Describe the auditee as the customer of the audit process and invite them to raise any issues during the audit that may need attention

Even after conducting employee awareness training, the pre-audit meeting, and the opening meeting of the audit itself, I often hear auditees tell me that the purpose of an internal audit is to catch them doing something wrong. Take one more opportunity to express to the auditees that they are the customers of the audit and that it may be to their advantage to make sure that process breakdowns are reported so that they can be addressed.

Depending on the concerns of the auditee, the "individual" opening meeting typically takes about five minutes or less. It is time well spent to ensure the success of the audit.

Interview techniques

After the environment of the audit has been well established, the interview can begin. But even after the "individual" opening meeting, the auditee may still be visibly nervous about the process. If this is the case, take a few additional moments to put the auditee at ease.

If the auditee is on edge, consider that they may be reflecting what they see in the auditor. What is your posture? Are you on the edge of your seat and invading their personal space? Are you standing with an aggressive posture? Take just a moment to evaluate whether or not you may be inadvertently causing the tension.

Spend a moment talking about something that the auditee finds interesting. In an internal audit, for example, you may know the auditee's hobbies and interests. Take a moment to talk about them.

As a last resort, ask the auditee if they have had a chance to take a break yet. Go to a cafeteria, a break room, or some other non-threatening location for a cup of coffee. During the "break," talk to the auditee about the types of things that you will be looking for when the audit begins. In doing so, you will be preparing the auditee for the audit and making them more confident about their ability to contribute to its success. Time is often your greatest enemy in an audit, but spending a few moments putting the auditee at ease is time well spent.

Then just learn everything you can about the process being audited. Start with a broad, open question to get the auditee talking to you.

- Can you walk me through this process?

- Please explain to me how this works.

- Help me understand those concerns that you have about this process (if concerns were raised during the opening meeting).

Throughout the interview, follow up with records and other documentation to verify conformance to ISO 9001:2000 and conformance to the organization's own documented system. The audit checklist should be used to record the results of the audit.

If a nonconformance is discovered during the interview, immediately bring it to the auditee's attention as tactfully as possible.

- I am looking for the design review minutes, but can't find them. Am I missing them or were the minutes not maintained?

- It looks like this Purchase Order was issued to a supplier that has not yet been approved.

- Let's get that down so that we can get it addressed one way or the other.

Try to avoid emotional words like discrepancy, failure, or nonconformance. Keep the environment positive—focused on the corrective action, not the finding.

At the end of the interview, summarize with the auditee the good findings as well as those that will need corrective action. The auditee should not be caught off guard at the closing meeting. Be sure that any finding or concern has been discussed prior to that time.

Basic communication skills

Much of internal auditing boils down to basic communication skills. But good communication skills are difficult to cultivate. It has been said that only 10% of communication is completed using words. Other components of communication, and how they impact the internal audit, are discussed below.

Tone of voice

Tone of voice can communicate a lot, whether or not we intend for that message to be conveyed. Take the expression, "You are kidding." Without hearing the tone of voice in which this phrase is made, the listener really doesn't know if this is an expression of total disbelief, great excitement, or anything in between.

In an audit situation, the auditee may hear something in the auditor's tone of voice that was not intended. I have been taught in the many communication classes that I have attended that communication is not complete until you repeat back in your own words what you think someone said and they agree with you. Therefore in trying to understand what the auditee was explaining, I used to say, "So you are telling me that you. . . ." I could not understand why folks were getting offended until an auditee asked why I would question his integrity. Apparently the tone in my voice conveyed something other than what I had intended.

If the auditee becomes defensive or aggressive during that audit, the auditor should be aware that he/she might have said something that simply got misunderstood. Think back over the conversation and try to resolve the issue.

Facial expressions

Facial expressions can communicate thoughts during an audit that the auditor really would not necessarily want communicated. Having worked with a number of youth groups through the years, my husband and I have learned to teach new adult advisors to look in the mirror every morning and practice that empathetic "I hear you" expression. If you do not have that one mastered pretty well, the utterly shocked "Have you lost your mind?" expression comes out before you know it and you lose the confidence of the teen.

The same concept applies in auditing. In helping a client in the automotive industry with their internal auditing, I approached several welders. The part they were working on was a safety-critical part that could greatly impact an individual's health in specific situations. It appeared to me that they had no process parameters available to monitor during the welding process, so I was curious how they verified the adequacy of the weld. When I asked, they carefully explained to me that they would try to physically pull the part apart. If they could pull it apart, it went in the rework bin. If they could not pull it apart, the part passed. It took years of audit experience to squash that "Have you lost your mind?" look.

In reality, the organization had never communicated to the welders the importance of that weld. If I had allowed my emotion to show in my expression, it probably would have inadvertently communicated that I thought the welders themselves were to blame for not understanding the critical nature of their work. But lack of adequate communication and training as well as the lack of adequate process controls were the causes of the problem, certainly not the intelligence level of the workforce.

The auditor should be careful that his/her expression does not shut the auditee down.

Body language, gestures, and posture

Body language, gestures, and posture can also communicate unintended messages during an audit. I have learned a lot through the years by asking my clients to critique my audit style after an audit. I have learned, for example, that I tend to sit on the edge of my chair. In most situations, this posture is not particularly a problem. But when I am auditing, it tends to make the auditee feel that I am being overly aggressive. I have learned to put the small of my back in the back of the chair when I sit down during the audit. It creates a more relaxed environment for everyone.

Auditors may also communicate an aggressive position through their body language. Standing with one leg cocked out and the clipboard propped on the other hip can create an intimidating environment.

Ignoring the auditee

It is easy during an audit to be thinking about so many things at one time, that you miss what the auditee is saying. Our brains are wired in a way that when we think back about something, our eyes tend to move up and away. It can be very irritating to auditees when the auditor does not pay attention to what they are saying. Be aware that when you think back, you may lose eye contact with the auditee. If you are aware of that tendency, it will help you prevent losing track of the conversation.

In an audit where the tension levels may be high, the auditor should especially be aware of how his/her communication style may be interpreted.

Keys to listening

A critical skill that any auditor must develop is that of carefully listening to the auditee. But there are obstacles that the auditor may have to overcome to truly hear what the auditee is trying to say.

Failure to separate the speaker from the topic

We all have a tendency to formulate an opinion about someone's point of view based on our history with that person or on our history with people that remind us of that person. These pre-conceived prejudices can be very detrimental to a successful audit.

From an internal audit perspective, perhaps the auditor has worked with the auditee in the past and does not have much respect for him/her. In this situation it is very easy to tune the auditee out and not hear the opportunities to improve the business that may be coming out of the audit.

Perhaps the best example here is an audit that I was observing for a client. It was apparent to me from the tension in the air that the internal auditor had a "history" with the auditee that prevented him from truly hearing everything that was being said. The auditee was leading the auditor to areas where improvement was needed, but the auditor would not express interest in following up on these points.

Prior to leaving the work area, I stepped in to ask the auditee if we had missed anything—if there was anything that he would like to see in the audit report to get the attention it deserved. The auditee answered quietly and thoughtfully, saying that there were a couple of things that he would like to add. He had been trying to tell people for years that he could run the line 25 feet a minute faster than any other shift and produce at least 10% fewer defects than any other shift. He thought he knew why, but couldn't get anyone to listen to him. Here is someone who actually wanted to share his secret with the entire organization and no one would listen.

The bottom line is that we were able to quickly verify his claims through an analysis of readily available, electronically generated data. Because the auditee had followed all procedures, but just ran the process in a different range of acceptable conditions, this was not an audit finding. But we cited an opportunity for improvement and provided the data to support it. As a result of this audit, the organization was able to calculate a return on this observation of over $650,000/ year in increased productivity and decreased rework. Rising above preconceived prejudices to listen to employees that others are not hearing can prove to be very profitable for the organization.

Anticipating specific information.

An interesting facet of communication is that what we hear is often filtered by what we think we are going to hear. If you think you already know the answer to a question, you tend to hear that answer regardless of what the speaker is saying.

If an auditor knows too much about the process being audited, it is difficult to hear the auditee over the opinion of the auditor. As strange as it sounds, I have witnessed it many times in the audits that I have observed. I have certainly been guilty of this myself. In helping clients implement the requirements of ISO 9001:2000, I will often help draft the quality manual and second tier quality procedures. I will then return to the organization to train their internal auditors. As part of that training, I may conduct a mock audit for the class to illustrate what an audit might look like. Many times I have caught myself recording an answer before the auditee has had a chance to answer the question. Once again, using auditors that are not responsible for the work being audited is truly critical to the success of an internal audit.

Thinking ahead

The primary reason for failing to hear someone is the habit of thinking ahead. When being introduced to someone for the first time, we fail to hear his/her name because we are too busy thinking about what we might say next to leave a great first impression. If we have a tendency to think ahead in everyday conversations, we will certainly have a tendency to think ahead during an audit.

As the auditee is speaking, he may mention something that you will want to follow up on. Just trying to remember what you want to ask next will keep you from hearing what the auditee is currently saying.

One technique to keep this from happening is to keep a blank sheet of paper in your lap during the audit. Let the note-taker take care of recording the facts observed during the audit. As the question-asker, you might just write down a key word or two that will remind you to follow up on important points. Having written down the reminder, you are free to listen carefully to the rest of what the auditee is saying. This is common in the "branching" technique that is discussed later in this chapter.

Permitting environmental hindrance

Often an internal audit will require that the auditor spend time in noisy or hot production areas. Having spent a large part of my career in the chemical industry along the Gulf Coast, I can tell you that some production areas are incredibly hot and very humid. If you are not acclimated to the heat and humidity, hearing what the auditee is saying will become more and more difficult the more miserable you become. You should interview operations personnel for ten or fifteen minutes, then go inside and catch up on your notes. Then go out again for ten or fifteen minutes and come back inside to catch up on your notes. Do not allow yourself to get so physically uncomfortable that you cannot truly listen to the auditee.

Being intimidated by complex technology

If the auditor is auditing a highly technical process, it is easy to tune the auditees out when they get into the technical aspects of their jobs. Nine times out of ten the auditee is just speaking their language. But being independent of the process being audited, the auditor is not typically expected to know the technical aspects of a process. A thorough document review should allow you to know the technical language well enough to at least follow the conversation. Beyond that, ask the auditee to help you understand more clearly how the process works.

One time out of ten, however, the auditee may simply be trying to intimidate you. If this is the case, remember who is in control. If they are trying to intimidate you, it is probably because they are intimidated by YOU. Handle them as you would an insecure auditee and see if the situation improves. If not, remember that you knew before you began the audit what records you were going to pull, how many, and what you would look for when you pulled them. Simply stick to the audit plan.

Rising above these obstacles to listening is important as you learn to optimize your audit skills.

Effective use of the checklist

As we discussed earlier, one drawback to a pre-developed "backbone" checklist is the tendency for audits to become stale over the years. The auditor must remember that the checklist is intended to be a guide for the audit, not a script. The experienced auditor should not read from the checklist, but should lay the checklist down and talk with the auditee to learn everything possible about the process being audited.

If two auditors are conducting the audit, the note-taker should be the one to maintain the notes and data on the checklist. The experienced question-asker should not even need to have a copy of the checklist during the actual audit. Both auditors should have worked with the checklist enough during the preparation phase to have a working knowledge of what is to be covered in the audit. The question-asker may then use either the branching technique or the tracing technique to learn everything possible about the process.

Branching Technique

In the branching technique, the auditor begins the audit by asking the auditee to explain the process being audited. As the auditee is describing the process, the auditor is recording on a blank piece of paper key points that he/she would like to follow up on. When the auditee reaches the end of his/her train of thought, the auditor can begin at the first point and learn everything possible about that point, pulling records along the way to verify conformance to ISO 9001:2000 and documented procedures. An audit of a corrective action process, for example, might lead to the following key points being jotted down.

- Customer complaints
- Internal audits
- External audits
- Product or service nonconformance reports (NCRs)
- Corrective action log
- Root cause analysis
- Action plan
- Verification
- Close out

When the auditee has finished describing the corrective action process, the auditor can then go to the top of the list of points and ask questions and pull records to fully understand each point. Of course, these questions will vary depending on where the audit leads, but examples of possible "branching" questions for each point are given below. (The points in parentheses are notes to the auditor rather than questions that the auditor might ask.)

- Customer complaints
  - ❑ Who typically receives customer complaints?
  - ❑ How are they recorded?
  - ❑ May I see that please?

❑ Who has the authority to decide whether a Corrective Action Request (CAR) is warranted?

❑ What action is taken if a CAR is not warranted? Is it recorded in some way? If so, may I see that please?

❑ If a CAR is warranted, how is the CAR then generated?

❑ (Review complaints at random and ask the auditee to pull any indicated CARs. Hold on to them to review, as you get deeper into the CAR process.)

- Internal audits

  ❑ How do you determine when a CAR is required following an internal audit?

  ❑ Who has the authority to make that decision?

  ❑ May I see the CARs that were generated following the last three audits? (Hold on to these CARs to review, as you get deeper into the CAR process.)

- External audits

  ❑ How is corrective action documented following an external audit?

  ❑ Who is responsible for responding to the registrar (or customer, if there were any customer audits)?

  ❑ May I see CARs that were generated following the last surveillance audit? (Hold on to these CARs to review, as you get deeper into the CAR process.)

- Product or service NCRs (Nonconformance Reports)

  ❑ How are product or service NCRs documented?

  ❑ Who reviews them to determine the need for a CAR?

  ❑ How is this evaluation made?

  ❑ May I see CARs that have been generated in the past year to reduce nonconforming product? (Hold on to these CARs to review, as you get deeper into the CAR process.)

- Corrective action log

  ❑ You mentioned that you keep a corrective action log. May I see it please?

  ❑ (Review the log briefly to evaluate timeliness of corrective actions. If CARs were not pulled during the previous conversations, select CARs at random off the log to review.)

- Root cause analysis

  ❑ Who is responsible for determining the root cause on the CAR?

  ❑ Has there been any root cause analysis training for these people?

  ❑ (Review the identified cause on the CARs that you have pulled to verify that the root cause of the problem was truly identified.)

- Action plan

  ❏ (Review the CARs to determine if the specified actions were sufficient to remove the root cause.)

- Verification

  ❏ Who is responsible for verifying that corrective actions have indeed been implemented and that they were effective?

  ❏ (Review CARs to ensure that they include evidence that the actions taken were EFFECTIVE.)

- Close out

  ❏ (Ensure that CARs were closed out without undue delay.)

When the question-asker has learned everything they can about the process, he/she turns to the note-taker and says, "Take it home. Have I missed anything or do you have anything else to add?" Where there are still blank spaces on the checklist, the note-taker follows up on those issues as well as other issues that came up during the audit that the question-asker did not explore.

Tracing Technique

Another technique used in auditing is called tracing. Though this technique is more applicable to a full systems audit, it can be used in a process audit as long as the auditee stays within the stated scope. Using this technique, the auditor either starts at the beginning of a process and works all the way through to the end, or begins at the end of the process and works backward. The typical example is selecting one lot of a product and auditing the entire quality management system as it relates to that one lot.

- Visually inspect the product if it is still at the facility. Is the product labeled and packaged in accordance with specified requirements?

- Is there any evidence of handling or storage damage?

- Was the final product testing completed in accordance with specified requirements?

- Were final test results in compliance with specifications?

- Do records indicate the personnel responsible for its release?

- Was in-process testing completed per specified requirements?

- Were in-process test results within specification limits?

- Do records indicate the personnel responsible for in-process release?

- Were process parameters within acceptable limits while the product was being made?

- What lots of raw materials or component parts were used in this product?

- Was incoming inspection performed on that material in accordance with specified requirements?

- Were incoming inspection results within specified limits?

- Do records indicate the personnel responsible for their release?

- Were instruments used in incoming, in-process, and final product testing properly calibrated?

Of course this example worked backward through a process. In a service industry, you may choose to take a service contract or project and work forward. This audit typically begins with the question, "Were customer requirements clearly defined for this project?" Then the auditor traces the project through each step to ensure that specified requirements were met.

Using one of these conversational styles of auditing is much more comfortable for the auditor and the auditee. New auditors will find that it is a little awkward to read questions off the checklist during the audit. After completing two or three audits, put the checklist down and start talking with the auditee. Not only is it more comfortable, but you will also learn a lot more during the audit. The auditee will tell you things you would have never dreamed to put on a checklist.

Sampling Data

Throughout the audit, the auditor will need to pull records to verify conformance to ISO 9001:2000 and to the organization's own documented system as well as the effectiveness of the process being audited. As discussed in

Chapter 5, the minimal sample size should be determined during the preparation phase of the audit and recorded on the audit checklist.

During the audit, the auditor must ensure that representative samples are selected at random. In auditing a corrective action process, for example, the auditor may want to pull Corrective Action Requests (CAR) from each of the inputs into that process. These inputs may include:

- Internal audits
- External audits
- Customer complaints
- Product or service nonconformity reports

Within each representative category, the samples should be pulled at random. Avoid the temptation to ask the auditee for an example of a CAR. Of course, the auditee will want to show you the very best example. If the auditee volunteers a sample, go ahead and audit it. Then pull 10 additional samples at random.

Handling difficult auditees

If the proper environment has been adequately established, handling difficult auditees is rarely an issue during an internal audit. But occasionally auditors may find themselves having to interview an auditee who is not excited about the audit process.

Most difficult auditees can be classified into one of four primary categories.

- The excessively nervous or anxious auditee

- The angry, resentful auditee

- The excessively proud auditee

- The auditee who is easily distracted by interruptions

We will discuss each of these categories as well as some techniques to ensure the success of the audit.

The nervous, anxious auditee

Techniques to put the nervous, anxious auditee at ease were discussed earlier in this chapter, so let's recap them.

- Often just clarifying the purpose of the audit goes a long way toward putting the auditee at ease.

- A few minutes of light conversation on a topic of interest to the auditee might help. In an internal audit, the auditor may know of a hobby the auditee enjoys or other topic of interest. If not, office pictures and wall decorations may make good conversation starters.

- As a last resort, the auditor and auditee can take a coffee break out of the work area. During the break, talk about the records that you will look at when the audit begins. Prepare the auditee for what is to be expected so that he/she does not feel that you are trying to trip them up.

- Sending the checklist to the auditees in advance is a good idea if there has been a history of nervous auditees in an area. Checklists should be based primarily on records and other facts and data. The auditor does not typically know in advance exactly which records will be reviewed, so the auditee cannot stage the audit using the checklist. The auditee does need to understand, however, that the checklist is simply a guide for the audit and will not be used as a script. The audit may go in other directions as the facts and data indicate. But it does provide a general idea of what the auditors will be looking for. Sending the checklist in advance provides some assurance that the auditor is not trying to trip up the auditees.

The angry, resentful auditee

The angry, resentful auditee is not necessarily a detriment to the audit. If the auditor can discover what is causing the anger, he/she may be able to use the audit to address the concerns. Regardless of the cause of the anger, remembering to treat the auditee with dignity and respect will go a long way toward resolving the situation. In handling this auditee, the auditor should find out, if possible, why the auditee is so angry, then the auditor should make every effort to use the audit resolve the issue, if possible. Some of the more common responses are given below.

- "This ISO stuff is the most ridiculous thing this organization has ever done. It is just a pile of useless paperwork and it keeps me from doing my job." As was discussed earlier, this is a wonderful opportunity to learn from the auditee where you can use the internal audit

to improve the process—and perhaps to bring significant improvement to the business as a whole. Explain
to the auditee that ISO 9001 was never intended to
weigh the organization down with excessive paperwork. Indeed, it is intended to streamline and optimize
processes. Ask for help in finding ways that the audit
can be used to make life a little easier on the auditee.

- "I have been in this stinking place for twelve hours a
  day, seven days a week for the past three months. Now
  you are here taking up another hour of my time. That
  only means I get to leave tonight at 9:00 instead of my
  usual 8:00. What about this are you having a hard time
  understanding?" Usually where there is anger, there is
  a decent reason for that anger.

To treat this auditee with respect is to use your audit
time wisely. Explain that if the auditee can just give you
five minutes to point you in the right direction, that
you would be happy to pull the records on your own
and get back with him in an hour or so to go over the
results. The auditee may respond with, "Okay, you have
your five minutes. Go." Good preparation will come in
handy here. Or the auditee may say, "There is no way
I would allow you to go through my records without
my being there." In this case, tell him that you would
actually prefer that he be there in case you have any
questions. You were just trying to save him some time.
Treating this auditee's time with respect will cause him
to return just enough respect to get the information
you need.

Make it a goal of your audit to find an opportunity to streamline this process to save this auditee some time in his job. You have an opportunity to create a real champion for the audit process.

- "We've jumped through every quality hoop there is to jump through. If it's got three or four letters, we've done it! TQM. APQP. FMEA. SPC. And now ISO. Why can't we just do our jobs?" The auditor should be armed with some specific, tangible improvements that have been generated through the implementation of ISO 9001 or through the internal audit process. First get the basics out of the way. "You really are right! But good, bad or indifferent, we have to keep our ISO 9001 registration if we want to keep doing business with our biggest customers. No ISO, no business. But that having been said, ISO really has done some pretty good things for us. . . ." Then talk about some of the successes that would impact the auditee. Stress that you can either play games with the audit, or really use it to try to make things better.

If auditees will not verbalize their frustrations, it is possible that they may just be a little nervous about the audit. Treat them as you would a nervous auditee and see if that helps alleviate the situation.

The excessively proud auditee

The excessively proud auditee is perhaps the most difficult to handle in the internal audit. This auditee has probably worked nights and weekends implementing processes that he/she is truly proud of. No one else has even noticed. AND NOW YOU ARE HERE TO LOOK AT ALL THEY HAVE DONE! They are truly excited about showing you everything they have accomplished.

To help understand the perspective of this auditee, remember the last time you redecorated your kitchen or bathroom yourself. (Contracting the work doesn't count.) God bless any visitor to your home! How excited were you to open and close cabinets, flush toilets, turn on faucets? How would you have felt if your friends and family responded to this demonstration with, "You missed a spot here. Why did you put this cabinet is such an inconvenient place? Have you noticed that this row of tiles is a little crooked?" Yet we do this all the time when we audit.

The first step in dealing with the proud auditee is to spend that first five minutes or so drooling over the work they have done. Typically, they are proud because they have a right to be proud. Give them the recognition that they need and deserve.

Then pull out the checklist. This is the only audit where I would recommend that you read directly off the checklist to maintain focus and order. Avoid words like "discrepancy," "failure" and "nonconformance" unless you want to see tears. Report findings in a way that would be perceived as adding a little extra value to a great process. I have discovered a substandard process while auditing a genuinely proud auditee only once in 21 years of auditing. Typically, these guys have worked hard and deserve a sincere, "nice job."

The easily distracted auditee

Handling the easily distracted auditee is not very complicated. Get the auditee away from the source of the distraction. The most common example of a distraction is the ringing telephone. Invite the auditee to a conference room to finish the audit. If the auditee is expecting an important call, ask him to forward his calls to an associate who can come get him if the call comes through.

Again, difficult auditees are not the norm. If the appropriate environment has been established, I have found most auditees in an internal audit to be quite helpful. Some have even been appreciative of the hard work performed by the auditor!

After the data-gathering phase of the audit is complete, the auditors must analyze that data, prepare an effective report, and conduct a closing meeting. These activities are addressed in Chapter 7.

CHAPTER 7

Reporting the Audit

Once data has been gathered, it is time to analyze the data to determine what will be classified as audit nonconformances, audit observations and opportunities for improvement. As discussed in Chapter 4, the auditor is not responsible for ensuring timely, thorough corrective action following an audit. That is the responsibility of the auditee's management who is in the best position to know what corrective action will be most effective.

How the auditor reports the findings, however, can either encourage or hinder timely, thorough corrective action. In this chapter, we will discuss how to classify audit findings, how to write effective Corrective Action Requests, how to document the audit report, and how to conduct an effective closing meeting.

Types of audit findings

Though each organization uses their own terminology, most have three general types of audit findings. For the sake of this discussion, I will define the terms that will be used in this chapter.

- A nonconformance is the breakdown, or partial breakdown, of a process in the quality management system. An audit nonconformance typically requires root cause analysis, root cause elimination, and/or a change in how the process is to be performed. As such, it requires a Corrective Action Request (or your organization's equivalent) to document the action taken. Registrars often call this type of finding a major nonconformance or a systemic finding.

  Examples of nonconformances may include:

  ❑ Of the 10 CAR's reviewed, only one showed evidence that the action taken was implemented and effective.

  ❑ There is no formal process to evaluate or re-evaluate suppliers of raw materials or component parts.

  ❑ Of the 10 pieces of equipment audited for compliance to the company's preventive maintenance requirements, eight were three months or more past due on required PM activities.

  ❑ Management review records do not show evidence that any action items were identified or completed during the review to result in continual improvement of the quality management system or its related processes, products, and services.

• An observation is a minor deviation from an otherwise well-implemented process. It is typically due to a minor oversight on the part of the auditee and is unlikely to result in nonconforming product or service. Root cause analysis is rarely required for observations; therefore a CAR is not typically warranted. Observations may be recorded on an Audit Action Item List (See Appendix D) to facilitate the analysis of trends. When multiple observations of a similar nature are noted during the audit or detected on the Audit Action Item List, the auditor or management representative may choose to initiate a CAR and treat the trend as a nonconformance. Registrars may refer to this type of finding as an observation or an isolated finding.

Examples of observations may include:

❑ Of the ten training records reviewed, one was not signed by the instructor.

❑ Of the three identified action items reviewed from the past management review meeting, one was not updated on the Action Item Log to show that it had been completed.

❑ Two of ten auditees interviewed were not completely aware of the organization's objectives and how their activities may impact our ability to meet those objectives.

❏ Though all five of the corrective actions reviewed from internal audits were thoroughly completed and verified as having been effective, two were not completed by the required completion date.

• An opportunity for improvement is a finding based on facts and data that indicates a potential improvement opportunity. Action is not required for an opportunity for improvement. Therefore, the auditor should include as much supporting data as possible to encourage action to be taken.

Internal auditors often struggle over the decision to classify a finding as a nonconformance or an observation. A good rule of thumb is this: If the finding requires the analysis and/or elimination of a root cause or if it requires a change to the current process, it is typically a nonconformance and a CAR should be initiated. If root cause analysis is not indicated, the finding is probably an observation. Observations should still be recorded on some type of Audit Action Item List, however, so that repetitive observations of a similar nature can be easily identified. Repetitive observations may indicate that the process is breaking down and a CAR may be indicated.

Writing effective Corrective Action Requests

When a Corrective Action Request (CAR) is indicated by the audit findings, the auditor typically has the responsibility for initiating the CAR. In some organizations, however, the management representative is responsible for reviewing audit findings and generating the CARs. Regardless of who initiates the CAR, it must contain vital information to encourage timely, thorough corrective action.

An example of a CAR form is provided in Appendix D and on the enclosed CD to facilitate your customization. The auditor is responsible for completing the CAR down through a description of the problem. If during the audit a probable root cause was discovered, the auditor may choose to record that on the CAR as well. The description of the problem must include two things if the auditee will respond in a positive manner. It must contain a reference to ISO 9001:2000 or the organization's own documentation and it must contain objective evidence to support the finding. If the location of the finding will help focus the corrective action in the right place, the auditor should provide that information as well.

The following examples of problem statements are poorly written:

- Employees do not seem to understand the policy statement or the organization's objectives. (Ref: 5.3 and 5.4.1)

- Document control of customer specifications needs a lot of improvement. (Ref: 4.2.3)

- Operators in the "B" unit are not running the process in accordance with the appropriate batch sheet. (Ref: 7.5)

- No one is reviewing customer satisfaction data. (Ref: 8.2.1)

- Nonconforming product is often not identified. (Ref: 8.3)

In each of these examples, the references to the standard are vague and there is no objective evidence to support the finding. The following examples include more specific references and the supporting objective evidence:

- Of the 10 employees interviewed, only five were familiar with our quality policy statement (Ref: 5.3.d) and only three were familiar with our quality objectives and how their activities impact our ability to meet those objectives. (Ref: 6.2.2.d)

- Of the 5 customer specifications reviewed in the QC Lab, three were at least one revision out of date and none were approved by the Customer Manager as required in BP-01. (Ref: 4.2.3.a/d)

- Of the five batch sheets reviewed in the "B" unit, all five showed the temperatures and pressures to be running outside the acceptable limits specified on the batch sheet. (Ref: 7.5.1.e) Auditor's note: Auditees suggested that the batch sheets were not revised after the last process improvement team implemented changes to the process.

- There is no defined process to review customer satisfaction data and initiate CARs where indicated. Responsibilities relative to this review have not been defined. (Ref: 8.2.1/8.4/8.5.1/5.5.1)

- During the audit, three rejected products were noted on the "D" line that were not identified or segregated. (Ref: 8.3 and BP-13, Section 5.4)

If the auditor is able to identify specific examples where these issues have caused nonconforming product to be shipped, premium freight to be paid, or other added costs to the operation, this additional information should be recorded on the CAR and presented at the closing meeting. For example:

- Of the five customer specifications reviewed in the QC Lab, three were at least one revision out of date and none were approved by the Customer Manager as required in BP-01. (Ref: 4.2.3.a/d)

  Auditor's note: Of the last three shipments returned from the customer, two were caused by obsolete specifications.

- There is no defined process to review customer satisfaction data and initiate CAR's where indicated. Responsibilities relative to this review have not been defined. (Ref: 8.2.1/8.4/8.5.1/5.5.1)

  Auditor's note: There are two specific areas that have been rated very low in the last two customer surveys: on-time delivery and customer service. We have lost at least two customers in the last six months due to these issues.

- During the audit, three rejected products were noted on the "D" line that were not identified or segregated. (Ref: 8.3 and BP-13, Section 5.4)

  Auditor's note: Three customer complaints were noted in the past six months due to our shipping product that had already been found to be reject.

Adding clear evidence indicating that a resolution of these issues will result in a return on investment will increase the probability of timely, thorough corrective action. Identification of the samples observed should be available in the completed audit checklist, which is typically maintained as part of the audit record. Including the sample identifications in the CAR encourages the auditee to "fix" the samples instead of correcting the process.

The audit report

The audit report should include a summary page describing the key information related to the audit. The summary page should include:

- Names of the auditors;
- Date(s) of the audit;
- Scope of the audit—including the process(es) audited with the applicable reference to ISO 9001:2000 and the areas or departments visited during the audit;
- Summary of nonconformances;
- Observations noted;
- Opportunities for improvement;
- Examples of outstanding performance or evidence of improvement since the last audit;
- Expectations for corrective action responses.

An example of an Audit Summary Report form can be found

in Appendix D and on the enclosed CD to facilitate your customization.

The auditor can then attach copies of the initiated CARs and the Audit Action Item List to the Audit Summary to complete the audit report. The key is providing the required information to the appropriate managers in a format that enables the report to be issued in a reasonable timeframe. To encourage timely corrective action, the report should be issued within 24 hours of the audit and should be distributed at or before the closing meeting.

When audit reports are issued two weeks or longer after the audit, they typically end up in a manager's "to-do" pile as a reminder to ask clarifying questions about the audit. The manager may not understand why something was a finding or may not understand the evidence to support the finding. So they make a note to follow up with their questions. One common aspect of most people's "to-do" piles is that they rarely get done.

The closing meeting

The closing meeting, with at least the managers of the areas audited, should be conducted within 24 hours of the audit. The purpose of the closing meeting is to ensure that those responsible for corrective action understand what the findings are, why they are findings, and what type of corrective action is required.

The audit report should be issued at the closing meeting and those in attendance should be given the opportunity to question and understand each finding in the report. If a manager leaves that meeting doubting the validity of a finding, the odds that timely corrective action will be taken are small.

If the auditors were able to uncover facts and data to support significant returns on investment (ROI) based on the indicated corrective action, that information should be provided at the closing meeting. It is rare that complete ROI data will be available in that timeframe, but any information leading to the calculation of returns should be provided to encourage those managers in attendance to take timely corrective action.

Summary of audit reporting

Though auditors do not have responsibility for corrective action following an internal audit, there are four things they can do to encourage such.

- Ensure that Corrective Action Requests contain the reference for the finding and specific objective evidence.

- Issue the audit report within 24 hours.

- Conduct a closing meeting with at least the manager(s) of the area(s) included in the audit.

- Provide information relating to ROI on the indicated corrective action if that information is available.

By following these suggestions, the auditors will have ensured that they have done everything in their power to facilitate timely, thorough corrective action following an internal audit.

CHAPTER 8

Follow-Up Audit Activities

ISO 9001:2000 requires that follow-up activities take place after the audit to ensure that corrective action taken was implemented and was effective at resolving the audit finding. In the audits I have performed, I have found that organizations are typically pretty good at verifying that corrective action was implemented, but are weak on verifying the effectiveness of that action.

The best individual to verify the effectiveness of the corrective action taken is one of the original auditors who recorded the finding. The auditors saw the process as it was before the audit and are typically in the best position to evaluate the effectiveness of the corrective action.

Perhaps the best method of discussing how to evaluate the effectiveness of corrective actions is to provide examples of what is acceptable and what is not for specific audit findings.

FINDING:

"Of the 10 employees interviewed, only five were familiar with our quality policy statement (Ref: 5.3.d) and only three were familiar with our quality objectives and how their activities impact our ability to meet those objectives. (Ref: 6.2.2.d)"

The corrective action defined for this finding required the organization to provide additional training for all of its employees to ensure that each understood the policy statement, the supporting objectives, and how their specific activities impacted the organization's ability to achieve the policy and the objectives. Given this defined action plan, many auditors verify the corrective action by pulling training records for a sample of employees at random and verifying that they had the required training. Such verification ensures that corrective action was taken, but falls short of verifying that the action taken was effective.

The only way to verify the effectiveness of the action taken is to re-audit this portion of the quality management system and see if the results indicate that the training provided was effective. This will involve questioning 10-20 employees at random throughout the organization and verifying that they are now aware of the policy and the objectives and how their specific activities impact the organization's ability to achieve both. The results of this re-audit should be recorded in the verification section of the CAR.

FINDING:

"Of the 5 customer specifications reviewed in the QC Lab, three were at least one revision out of date and none were approved by the Customer Manager as required in BP-01. (Ref: 4.2.3.a/d)"

In this case, the cause of the problem was determined to be that the facility audited was not on the corporate Customer Service Department distribution list for customer specifications. As such, the specifications were not being updated at this facility.

A superficial re-audit of this finding would verify that the five customer specifications have now been updated and are properly approved. This verification activity does not even fully verify that adequate corrective action was taken, much less that the corrective action was effective.

A slightly better approach would be to verify that the distribution list in the Customer Service Department had been updated to include this particular facility and that that all customer specifications in the Lab had been updated. Still, this activity only verifies that the corrective action was TAKEN, but supplies no evidence to support that the action was EFFECTIVE.

To verify the effectiveness of the action taken, the auditor should allow the new process to be implemented on several specification revisions. The auditor can then identify the last three to five spec changes from the Customer Service Department and verify that all appropriate copies in the facility were properly approved and issued. This data should then be recorded in the verification section of the CAR.

FINDING:

"Of the five batch sheets reviewed in the "B" unit, all five showed the temperatures and pressures to be running outside the acceptable limits specified on the batch sheet. (Ref: 7.5.1.e) Auditor's note: Auditees suggested that the batch sheets were not revised after the last process improvement team recommended changes to the process."

The cause of the finding in this case was determined to be that the quality improvement process used at this facility did not include the updating of applicable documentation when changes to the process are made. So the organization updated its quality improvement process to include this step before the team disbanded.

A superficial verification of this audit finding would be to verify that the quality improvement process had indeed been updated and that batch sheets had been revised to reflect current operating conditions. Again, such verification would prove that corrective action has been taken and that the current batch sheets were correct, but would not ensure that the change to the quality improvement process has been effectively implemented to provide adequate documentation for future process changes.

The auditor should not only do the verification described above, but should also allow enough time to pass for several quality improvement teams to complete their assigned task, if possible. The auditor should then verify that any changes recommended by the team resulted in appropriate documentation revisions to reflect those changes.

FINDING:

"There is no defined process to review customer satisfaction data and initiate CARs where indicated. Responsibilities relative to this review have not been defined. (Ref: 8.2.1/8.4/8.5.1/5.5.1)"

As a result of this audit finding, the organization updated its customer satisfaction procedure to include responsibility for reviewing the data to determine the need for corrective or preventive action, how that review should be conducted and how the CAR or PAR should be initiated.

To effectively verify this action, the auditor should ensure that the procedure had indeed been revised and appropriately issued. He/she should then re-audit the next customer survey results to ensure that the data was reviewed as documented and that action was taken where indicated by the data.

FINDING:

"During the audit, three rejected products were noted on the "D" line that were not identified or segregated. (Ref: 8.3 and BP-13, Section 5.4)"

In this case, the organization found that the procedure for the control of nonconforming products was well written, but was not being followed. The root cause was found to be that employees were not aware of what the procedure required. The corrective action included not just training employees on the current procedure for the control of nonconforming products, but updating the document control procedure so that appropriate personnel are made aware of the changes and adequate training is provided where required.

To verify the effectiveness of this CAR, the auditor should indeed re-audit the control of nonconforming product to ensure that reject products were now being identified and segregated per the procedure. But the auditor should also find out if the document control procedure has been updated and properly issued to specify how procedural changes will be communicated to appropriate personnel and how and when appropriate training is provided. The auditor should then pull recent document changes to ensure that the new process is being followed.

Each of these examples illustrates that the auditor must go beyond verifying that the symptoms have been fixed. The auditor must ensure that the process has been changed so that similar process breakdowns are not likely to occur in the future.

Summary of Effective Internal Auditing

This book was intended to provide specific tools and techniques to facilitate internal audits that are effective at improving the business and its bottom line. The key points in such an effective audit process include:

- Establishing an environment where managers and employees value the internal audit as a critical tool in its overall quality improvement strategy.

- Focusing on the successes of an internal audit—not just the number of findings.

- Finding ways to communicate those successes throughout the organization so that managers and employees are aware of the benefits that have been derived from the internal audit process.

- If possible, calculating the return on investment for corrective actions taken as a result of internal audits and communicating these successes throughout the organization.

- Ensuring that auditors adequately prepare for the audit so that they will know before they conduct the audit what records will be pulled, how many will be pulled and what will be reviewed when they pull them.

- Ensuring that auditors are trained to verify that desired outputs of the processes are clearly defined and that inputs into the process are provided to ensure that the process can achieve the desired outputs.

- Issuing the audit report within 24 hours of the audit.

- Ensuring that any CARs initiated as a result of the audit contain an appropriate reference to the standard or the organization's own documented procedures as well as clear objective evidence.

- Conducting a closing meeting with all applicable managers to ensure that issues in the report are clearly understood.

- Thoroughly verifying that any required corrective actions have been EFFECTIVELY completed before closing them out.

It is sincerely my desire that these tools and techniques will help you to improve the effectiveness of your internal audit process and achieve measurable benefits for your organization and its bottom line.

Appendix A

Sample Process Models

- Quality planning
- Management review
- Competence, awareness and training
- Maintenance
- Planning for product realization
- Customer-related processes
- Design and development control
- Purchasing
- Product or service realization
- Control of monitoring and measuring equipment
- Customer satisfaction
- Internal quality audit
- Monitoring and measurement of product
- Corrective action
- Preventive action

Quality Planning
(Reference ISO 9001:2000, Clause 5.4.2)

Possible Inputs:	Outputs:
<ul><li>Objectives</li><li>Business strategies</li><li>Customer needs and requirements</li><li>Statutory and regulatory requirements</li><li>Product performance data</li><li>Process performance data</li><li>Lessons learned</li><li>Opportunities for improvement</li></ul>	<ul><li>Required skills and knowledge needed to achieve objectives</li><li>Defined responsibility and authority for implementing process improvement plans</li><li>Required resources</li><li>Metrics for evaluating performance improvement</li></ul>

Possible criteria to evaluate the effectiveness of the quality planning process given the desired outputs:

- Specific, tangible successes from the quality planning process
- Improving metrics used to evaluate performance improvement

Management Review
(Reference ISO 9001:2000, Clause 5.6)

Possible Inputs:	Outputs:
<ul><li>Internal and external audit results (*)</li><li>Customer feedback (i.e.: survey results, complaints, etc.) (*)</li><li>Process performance and product conformity metrics (i.e.: productivity, efficiency, on-time delivery, scrap rates, rework, etc.) (*)</li><li>Status of corrective and preventive actions (*)</li><li>Follow-up actions from previous reviews (*)</li><li>Changes that could affect the QMS (*)</li><li>Recommendations for improvement (*)</li><li>Status and results of the quality policy, objectives and improvement opportunities (*)</li><li>Benchmark activities</li><li>Marketplace evaluations and strategies</li><li>Sales performance</li><li>Cost of quality data</li></ul>	<ul><li>Improvement of the effectiveness of the QMS and its processes (*)</li><li>Improvement of the product or service (*)</li><li>Resource needs (*)</li><li>Performance improvement objectives for the organization</li><li>Strategies and initiatives for marketing</li><li>Strategies and initiatives for improvement in customer satisfaction</li><li>Management review meeting minutes (*)</li></ul>
	(*) – Required by ISO 9001:2000

Possible criteria to evaluate the effectiveness of the management review process given the desired outputs:

- Timely, thorough completion of identified action items
- Specific improvements to the QMS and its processes, customer satisfaction ratings, or the organization's product or service resulting from management review

Competence, Awareness and Training
(Reference ISO 9001:2000, Clause 6.2)

Possible Inputs:	Outputs:
<ul><li>Defined competence requirements</li><li>Career planning needs</li><li>Defined individual training needs (i.e., new employee training checklists, training plans, refresher training requirements, etc.)</li><li>Defined organizational training needs (i.e., quality improvement tools, team building skills, internal audit training, knowledge of new or changed processes, etc.)</li><li>Qualified trainers (or sponsors/mentors)</li><li>Applicable procedures</li><li>Applicable work instructions</li><li>Training evaluation criteria</li><li>Applicable organizational or departmental objectives</li></ul>	<ul><li>Qualified and competent personnel</li><li>Training records</li></ul>

Possible criteria to evaluate the effectiveness of the training process given the desired outputs:

- Evaluations of the training process provided by new employees

- Process performance data (i.e.: Have process measurements shifted after new personnel have been trained? Examples differ depending on the position being audited, but may include: productivity and efficiency ratings (operations), off-spec or reworked product (operations), late deliveries of raw materials (purchasing), repetitive verification or validation failures (design), poor performance against design budget and timing requirements (design), repetitive customer complaints for late deliveries due to accepting shipment requirements that could not be met (sales/order entry), etc.
- Performance evaluations of new employees showing similar deficiencies
- Conformance with defined organizational or departmental objectives

Maintenance
(Reference ISO 9001:2000, Clause 6.3)

Possible Inputs:	Outputs:
• Qualified, competent maintenance personnel (See 6.2) • List of equipment to be maintained • Preventive maintenance schedule • Work orders with required information • Controlled procedures, work instructions, or equipment manuals (See 4.2.3) • Required tools and gages • Spare parts inventory • Organizational or departmental objectives	• Equipment that runs well when needed • Maintenance records

Possible criteria to evaluate the effectiveness of the maintenance process given the desired outputs:

• Trends in uptime or downtime
• Number of emergency breakdowns
• Missed shipments due to equipment failures
• Conformance with the organizational or departmental objectives

Planning of Product or Service Realization
(Reference ISO 9001:2000, Clause 7.1)

Possible Inputs:	Outputs:
• Customer requirements and expectations (See 7.2) • Application of the product • Process / product requirements • Acceptance criteria for product requirements • Competence of personnel • Current documentation (i.e.: forms, work instructions, procedures, etc.) • Process / equipment capability • Work environment • Applicable regulatory, statutory and industry-specific requirements	• Defined process steps • Control measures • Acceptance criteria • Training needs • Required equipment • Defined methods • Adequate information • Controlled process changes • Verified and validated product • Verified and validated process changes

Possible criteria to evaluate the effectiveness of the planning process given the desired outputs:

• Evaluation of the ability of the outputs to meet the input requirements
• Was adequate training provided for the last new or changed product or process?
• Were appropriate information, methods, procedures, specifications, etc. provided to operations, QA, maintenance, or purchasing personnel when the last new or changed product or process was implemented?
• Was the past new or changed product or process properly verified and validated to show that customer requirements were met?

Customer-Related Processes
(Reference ISO 9001:2000, Clause 7.2)

Possible Inputs:	Outputs:
• Qualified and competent sales, marketing, and order entry personnel • Customer requirements and expectations • Product application • Market research information • Competitor analysis or benchmark information • Regulatory, statutory and industry-specific requirements • Organizational or departmental objectives (i.e., on-time delivery performance, orders accepted within specified lead times, etc.)	• Well-defined needs and expectations communicated to applicable personnel in the organization • Product specifications • Defined packaging requirements • Defined delivery requirements (i.e.: quantity and ship dates) • Defined shipping mode • Defined documentation requirements • Capacity requirements • Records of review

Possible criteria to evaluate the effectiveness of the process of defining and reviewing customer requirements given the desired outputs:

• Conformance to lead time requirements
• Customer complaints due to poorly-defined requirements
• Delivery performance
• Process capability metrics
• Conformance with organizational or departmental objectives

Design and Development Control
(Reference ISO 9001:2000, Clause 7.3)

Possible Inputs:	Outputs:
• Qualified and competent design personnel • Customer requirements and expectations • Marketplace needs and expectations • Supplier capabilities • Product application • Statutory and regulatory requirements • Industry codes of practice • Needs of those internal customers who will be receiving the output • Lessons learned from previous experiments • Timing and scheduling requirements • Budget/cost requirements • Organizational or departmental objectives	• Product specifications / drawings with acceptance criteria • Process specifications • Incoming material specifications • Test requirements and specifications • Training requirements • Design verification and validation results • Data demonstrating conformance with design input

Possible criteria to evaluate the effectiveness of the design and development process given the desired outputs:

• Verification / validation performance (first time pass rates)
• Operations, QA, purchasing, maintenance, etc. getting required information for new or changed products and processes
• Process capabilities
• On-time, on-budget performance
• Conformance with organizational and departmental objectives

Purchasing
(Reference ISO 9001:2000, Clause 7.4)

Possible Inputs:	Outputs:
• Qualified, competent purchasing personnel • Raw material specifications • Production schedule • Required delivery dates • Required quantities • Packaging, shipping, and paperwork requirements for incoming materials • Supplier qualification requirements • Supplier re-evaluation requirements • Pricing requirements • Incoming documentation requirements • Purchasing software • Organizational / departmental objectives	• Acceptable incoming products arriving on time at a competitive price • Purchase orders, contracts, or other purchasing records

Possible criteria to evaluate the effectiveness of the purchasing process given the desired outputs:

• Delivery performance of incoming products
• Pass rate at incoming inspection
• Performance of incoming products in operations
• Conformance with organizational / departmental objectives

Product or Service Realization
(Reference ISO 9001:2000, Clause 7.5)

Possible Inputs:	Outputs:
<ul><li>Qualified, competent operations / service personnel</li><li>Acceptable incoming products</li><li>Properly maintained process equipment</li><li>Calibrated instrumentation</li><li>Utilities</li><li>Suitable work environment</li><li>Clear work instructions</li><li>Understandable process specifications</li><li>Product specifications</li><li>Production schedule</li><li>Identification / traceability requirements</li><li>Handling and storage requirements</li><li>Packaging and shipping requirements</li><li>Organizational / departmental objectives</li></ul>	<ul><li>Acceptable finished product delivered on time at a competitive price</li><li>Completed process and shipping records</li></ul>

Possible criteria to evaluate the effectiveness of the product/service realization process given the desired outputs:

- Scrap or rework rates
- Delivery requirements
- Customer complaints for product quality
- Conformance with organizational / departmental objectives

Control of Monitoring and Measuring Devices
(Reference ISO 9001:2000, Clause 7.6)

Possible Inputs:	Outputs:
• Qualified, competent calibration personnel • Defined calibration methods (including: frequency of checks, calibration method, acceptance criteria, actions to take if instruments are out of calibration, etc.) • Instruments to be calibrated • Instrument accuracy requirements • Traceable standards • Suitable environment (i.e., temperature and humidity requirements, if applicable) • Organizational / departmental objectives	• Instrumentation that consistently meets accuracy requirements • Calibration records or reports

Possible criteria to evaluate the effectiveness of the calibration process given the desired outputs:

- Frequency of instrumentation found to be out of calibration
- Compliance to the calibration schedule
- Conformance with organizational / departmental objectives

Customer Satisfaction
(Reference ISO 9001:2000, Clause 8.2.1)

Possible Inputs:	Outputs:
• Customer surveys • Customer complaints • Direct communications with the customers • Focus group results • Reports from consumer organizations • Sector and industry studies • Benchmark studies • Defined process and responsibilities for reviewing, analyzing, and responding to customer satisfaction data • Organizational / departmental objectives	• Measurement of the customers' perception of the organization's ability to meet customer requirements • Actions to improve customer satisfaction • Records relating to customer satisfaction

Possible criteria to evaluate the effectiveness of the customer satisfaction process given the desired outputs:

• Trends in customer satisfaction measures
• Effective completion of appropriate action items based on the customer satisfaction data
• Conformance to organizational / departmental objective

Internal Audits
(Reference ISO 9001:2000, Clause 8.2.2)

Possible Inputs:	Outputs:
• Qualified, competent internal auditors • Audit schedule • Audit plan • "Backbone" audit checklist • Identified standards and procedures against which to audit • Results from previous audits • Auditees • Defined process and responsibilities for addressing audit findings • Organizational / departmental objectives	• Evidence of compliance with ISO 9001:2000 and the organization's QMS • Opportunities for continual improvement

Possible criteria to evaluate the effectiveness of the internal audit process given the desired outputs:

• Specific improvements that were initiated through the audit process
• Conformance with the audit schedule
• Return on investment of corrective actions following internal audits
• Conformance with organizational / departmental objectives

Product Monitoring and Measurement
(Reference ISO 9001:2000, Clause 8.2.4)

Possible Inputs:	Outputs:
• Qualified, competent inspection personnel • Defined product monitoring and measurement requirements • Defined sample points in the process • Inspections required to be witnessed or performed by regulatory bodies • Raw material and product specifications or other defined acceptance criteria • Documented test methods • Calibrated instrumentation • Reagents and other test materials • Organizational / departmental objectives	• Accurate, timely test and inspection results to verify the degree to which products and services meet specified criteria • Product monitoring and measurement records

Possible criteria to evaluate the effectiveness of the product monitoring and measurement process given the desired outputs:

- Compliance with defined inspection and test requirements
- Timeliness of inspection and test results
- Accuracy of inspection and test results (i.e.: round robin test results, gage R&R results, etc.)
- Returned product that was verified as acceptable before it was shipped
- Conformance with organizational / departmental objectives

Corrective Action
(Reference ISO 9001:2000, Clause 8.5.2)

Possible Inputs:	Outputs:
• Internal or external audit findings • Customer complaints/feedback • Records of nonconforming product • Nonconformances related to suppliers' goods or services • Management review outputs • Organizational / departmental objectives	• Tangible improvements to the quality management system, its related processes and the organization's product or service

Possible criteria to evaluate the effectiveness of the corrective action process given the desired outputs:

- Percentage of corrective actions completed in a timely manner (i.e.: by the estimated completion date)
- Tangible improvements to the business resulting from the corrective action process (i.e.: less scrap, less rework, increased productivity, decreased premium freight charges, decreased costs of quality failures, improved equipment reliability, etc.)
- Trends in customer satisfaction data
- Conformance to organizational / departmental objectives

Preventive Action
(Reference ISO 9001:2000, Clause 8.5.3)

Possible Inputs:	Outputs:
• Management review results • Failure Mode and Effects analysis • Fault tree analysis • Customer satisfaction measurements • Market analysis • Process measurements (including processes that provide early warning of approaching out-of-control conditions – i.e.: SPC) • Quality improvement team recommendations • Employee suggestions • Opportunities for improvement identified during internal audits	• Tangible improvements to the quality management system, its related processes and the organization's product or service

Possible criteria to evaluate the effectiveness of the preventive action process given the desired outputs:

- Percentage of preventive actions completed in a timely manner (i.e.: by the estimated completion date)
- Specific improvement team successes
- Tangible improvements to the business resulting from the corrective action process (i.e.: less scrap, less rework, increased productivity, decreased premium freight charges, decreased costs of quality failures, improved equipment reliability, etc.)
- Trends in customer satisfaction data
- Conformance to organizational / departmental objectives

Appendix B

Sample Audit Checklist

Instructions for use:

- This checklist is intended to be a starting point for developing a backbone checklist that is customized for your organization. Please see Chapter 5 for a discussion on how to reword this checklist to meet the specific needs of your organization.

- The comments in carets <> represent those comments that will definitely need to be customized for an organization. Examples of information you will find in carets include:

  - <Your organization> - When initiating the customization of your checklist, you may choose to use the "find and replace" command to find this phrase and replace it with the name of your organization.

  - <X> - This will need to be replaced with an appropriate sample size for your organization. The sample size is typically 3-10, but will vary depending on the time it will take to audit a sample and the number of samples there are to choose from. If your organization performs management review annually, for example, a sample size of 3 would be a bit excessive.

  - Other comments in carets are examples of specific items the auditor might look for. Because these will differ from organization to organization, you will need to select those that relate to you and delete the others.

- Those comments in parentheses () are notes to the auditor and are not intended to be read to the auditee. These comments typically provide tips to the auditor on what records to pull, how many to pull and what to look for when they pull them. Of course the checklist is not intended to be used as a script for the audit, but many new auditors will stay pretty close to the checklist until they become more comfortable with the audit process.

- Those questions marked with an asterisk (*) are those that should be included in every process audit. The two categories that have asterisks are 4.2.2 (quality manual) and 4.2.4 (control of records). In each process audit, the auditor should compare the applicable section in the quality manual to other related documentation to look for any conflicting information. Control of records will be evaluated in each process audit as well. Every time an auditor pulls a record, he/she should verify that the record was readily retrievable, legible, and filed in accordance with the documented procedure.

- Finally, audit matrices are used throughout this checklist to facilitate the evaluation of records. Matrices will instruct the auditor on what records should be pulled and what should be evaluated when the records are reviewed. Several matrices include split cells. (Reference the matrix in Section 7.6 for measuring and monitoring devices, for example.) The top half of the cell can be completed during audit preparation to specify what the auditor SHOULD find for that given item. The bottom half can be completed during the audit itself to record what WAS found. Frequency of checks, for example, has been split on this matrix. In preparing for the audit, the auditor can record in the top half of the cell what frequency is required by the procedure for a specific instrument. All the information needed to verify compliance to the procedure will then be available on the matrix preventing a lot of fumbling through procedures during the audit.

Audit matrices facilitate the compliance piece of the internal audit to allow for time to evaluate the effectiveness of the process.

Audit Checklist – ISO 9001:2000

Audit date: _____

Auditor(s): _____

Process audited: _____

Procedures audited: _____

Areas audited: _____

_____

_____

_____

_____

Notes:

REFERENCE	QUESTIONS	EVIDENCE	CAR #, if Applicable
CLAUSE 4	QUALITY MANAGEMENT SYSTEM		
4.1	General Requirements 1. The requirements of this section are audited as a part of the rest of this audit checklist. 　a. Verification that processes in the quality management system have been identified along with their sequence and interaction is addressed in Section 4.2.2. 　b. Verification that criteria and methods have been determined to effectively implement each of these processes is addressed as each process is audited. 　c. Verification of available resources and necessary information is addressed in Clauses 5 and 6 as well as in auditing the effectiveness of each process. 　d. The monitoring, measuring, and analyzing of each process is addressed as the effectiveness of that process is being audited. These issues are further addressed in Clauses 8.4 and 8.5.	No notes required. See notes related to the audit of each process.	

4.2.1	Documentation Requirements	No notes required. See notes related to the audit of each process.	
	1. The requirements of this section are audited as part of the rest of this audit checklist. Required documentation is audited as each process is audited.		
4.2.2	Quality Manual		
4.2.2.a	1. *Does the quality manual cover the requirements of ISO 9001:2000? (During audit preparation, compare the quality manual to the requirements of ISO 9001:2000 and verify that all requirements have been addressed. Note any exceptions to the right.)		
4.2.2.a	2. *Are any exclusions to ISO 9001:2000 clearly stated in the manual along with adequate justification? <Exclusions may include only those requirements in Clause 7, but must be clearly justified in the manual.>		

4.2.2.b	3. *Does the quality manual reference or include supporting procedures? Do procedures agree with the quality manual? (During audit preparation for each process, compare the procedures to the quality manual to verify conformance. Note any exceptions to the right.)		
4.2.2.c	4. Does the quality manual include a description of the processes in the quality management system, their sequence and how they interact with other processes?		
4.2.3	Control of Documents		
	1. Who is responsible for the control of each type of document at <your organization>? How does this process work? (Study the procedures and interview auditees to understand the process. Ensure that responsibilities are clearly understood throughout the organization. Note any exceptions to the right.)		
4.2.3.b	2. Describe the process for ensuring that each document is reviewed and updated as necessary.		

4.2.3.a 4.2.3.c 4.2.3.d	3. (Select up to five types of documents in each area audited and complete the "Control of Documents" audit matrix following this section.)		
4.2.3.e	4. (During the audit, were any documents noted that were illegible or not readily identifiable? If so, note the document numbers to the right.)		
4.2.3.f	5. How are external documents controlled? (Verify that any documents of external origin are identified and that their distribution is controlled. List to the right those documents that were verified as well as any that were not controlled.)		
4.2.3.g	6. How are obsolete documents that have been retained suitably identified as being obsolete? (Pull examples and verify conformance.)		

4.2.3 – Process Effectiveness	7. Is the document control system cumbersome? Does it prevent employees from updating documents as needed because the approval and issuing processes are too complicated? Is there anything that should be done to make the document control process more effective? (Discuss with the auditees. Record any specific opportunities for improvement to the right and as observations in the audit report.)	

CONTROL OF DOCUMENTS – AUDIT MATRIX

Department audited: _____

Type of Document Audited	Number of documents observed	Number that were readily available	Number that were properly approved		Number that were the current issue	Number with the nature of the latest revision identified	Comments

4.2.4	Control of Quality Records		
	1. *(Throughout the audit, verify that records being presented to the auditor have been identified as quality records in the procedures. Note any exceptions to the right.)		
4.2.4	2. *(Throughout the audit, verify that records are legible, readily retrievable and stored in a way that protects their fitness for use. Have responsibilities for record collection and maintenance been clearly defined and documented? Are they understood?)		
4.2.4	3. *(Where records are stored electronically, verify that the data is backed up to prevent its loss.)		
4.2.4	4. *(Verify that retention times have been defined for quality records and that records are retrievable throughout that time.)		

CLAUSE 5	MANAGEMENT RESPONSIBILITY				
5.1, 5.2, 5.3, and 5.4	Management Commitment, Customer Focus, Quality Policy, Quality Planning 1. (Interview senior management at <your organization> to verify commitment to the quality management system. Include the following questions:				
5.1.b	a. What is the quality policy for <your organization>?				
5.3.b	b. (Does it specify a commitment to comply with requirements and to the continual improvement of the effectiveness of the quality management system?)				
5.3.c	c. (Does the policy serve as a framework for supporting objectives?)				
5.3.e/5.6.1	d. How is the policy reviewed to ensure its continued suitability? (Pull management review records to verify compliance.)				

5.3.d	e. How have you communicated the policy throughout the organization?				
5.1.a	f. How do you communicate the importance of meeting customer and regulatory/statutory requirements?				
5.4.1	g. What measurable objectives have been established to support the policy and to verify the effectiveness of the quality management system?				
5.2	h. Which of these objectives demonstrate a customer focus for the organization?				
5.4.1	i. How are objectives pushed down to applicable levels and functions at <your organization>?				
5.4.2.a	j. How are objectives tracked and monitored?				

5.4.2.a	k. What planning process exists for meeting these objectives?		
5.4.2.a and effectiveness of establishing objectives	l. May I see our progress toward these objectives? (Are objectives being achieved? If not, what actions are taken to improve the quality management system? Pull action plans for these objectives to ensure that action is being taken to achieve them.)		
5.4.2.a/5.6.1	m. If objectives are being achieved, how are they reviewed for opportunities of continual improvement? (Pull any available records to verify that this is being done.)		
5.4.2.b	n. When changes are made to the organization <i.e.: reorganizations, new processes or product lines, etc.>, what steps are taken to protect the integrity of the quality management system?		

5.3.d	2. Is the quality policy statement understood throughout <your organization>? (Ask <X> employees throughout the audit if they are aware of the statement, if they can state it in their own words, and if they know how it relates to their jobs.)	
6.2.2.d (outside this clause, but this is a good time to audit this requirement)	3. Are the objectives also understood throughout the organization as well as how employees' activities impact those objectives? (When asking employees about the policy statement, also ask them if they are aware of any objectives that may impact their job and how their activities impact the organization's ability to meet those objectives.)	
5.5	Responsibility, Authority and Communication	
5.5.1	Responsibility and Authority	
	1. Are responsibilities and authorities clearly defined and understood for all employees who affect quality? (Verify throughout audit preparation that procedures clearly define responsibility and/or authority for each task. Note any exceptions to the right.)	

5.5.1 and 4.2.3	2. \<If job descriptions are used to define responsibilities and authorities...\> Are job descriptions current and properly approved? (Select \<X\> job descriptions at random and verify that they are current and properly approved.)			
5.5.2	Management Representative 1. Is there a clearly defined Management Representative? Is he/she a member of management?			
5.5.2.c	2. How does the Management Representative ensure the promotion of awareness of customer requirements throughout the organization?			
5.5.3	3. What methods are used to communicate the effectiveness of the quality management system to employees in the organization? \<i.e.: Employee meetings? Communication boards? Monitors? Newsletters? Etc.\>			

5.6	Management Review 1. How does management review the status of the quality management system at planned intervals to determine its suitability, adequacy, and effectiveness?
	2. Does the required agenda include:
5.6.2.e	a. Follow-up actions from previous management reviews?
5.6.2.a	b. Results of audits?
5.6.2.b	c. Customer feedback?
5.6.2.c	d. Data related to process performance or product conformity?
5.6.2.d	e. Status of corrective and preventive actions?
5.6.2.f	f. Planned changes that could impact the QMS?
5.6.2.g	
5.6.1	

	g. Recommendations for improvement? h. Review of the quality policy and objectives to assess opportunities for improvement and the need for any changes?	
5.6.1 and 5.6.3	3. Select the last <X> management reviews and complete the matrix at the end of this section.	
5.6 - Effectiveness	4. During the past year, what specific improvements to the QMS, its processes, or the product have been initiated or made as a result of management review? Have resource requirements been adequately addressed? (Discuss with the auditee and look for evidence in the management review records. Note evidence of improvement to the right. Also note any opportunities for improvement and site them as observations in the audit report.)	

MANAGEMENT REVIEW – AUDIT MATRIX

Management review meetings audited	Was it held at the required interval?	Were required attendees present?	Were required agenda items covered?	Were identified action items completed?

CLAUSE 6	RESOURCE MANAGEMENT			
6.1	Provision of Resources			
	1. (Verify throughout the audit that adequate resources have been provided to effectively implement and improve the quality management system.)			
6.2	Human Resources			
	1. How are competency requirements and training needs identified for new and current employees? How is training evaluated for effectiveness? (Study any documentation and interview auditees to understand the process.)			
6.2.2.a 6.2.2.b 6.2.2.c 6.2.2.d 6.2.2.e	2. (Pull training records for <X> new employees – or employees new to their position – who have been trained in the previous year and complete the matrix on the following page. Be sure to include any applicable management, technical, and administrative personnel who affect product quality as well as operators, lab technicians, and maintenance personnel.)			

NEW EMPLOYEE TRAINING – AUDIT MATRIX

New employee	Were competency requirements defined?	Was required training provided?	Was effectiveness of training evaluated?	Did training include knowledge of company objectives and the employee's impact on them?	Comments

Verification of input				
6.2.2	3. How are trainers selected? What instruction, if any, are they given to ensure that training is effective?			
	4. How are on-going training needs identified for existing employees? (Pull records for <X> current employees and verify conformance to planned arrangements.)			
6.2.2.c	5. How is the training process evaluated for effectiveness? (Pull records to verify conformance.) Is there anything that needs to be done to make the process more effective? (Discuss with auditees and new employees. Record any specific opportunities for improvement as observations on the audit report.)			
6.3	Infrastructure 1. Describe the maintenance process. Does it include preventive, predictive, and emergency maintenance as appropriate? (Study any documentation and interview auditees to understand the process.)			

6.3.b	2. How is the preventive maintenance (PM) scheduled? By whom? May I see the PM schedule? (Pull records for <X> pieces of equipment and verify conformance to the schedule.	
Effectiveness of 6.3.b	3. What measures do you track to evaluate the effectiveness of the maintenance process? (Review <work orders, downtime reports, number of equipment failures, etc.> for repetitive equipment breakdowns or other opportunities to improve the maintenance process.	
Effectiveness of 6.3.b	4. (Interview operations personnel or other internal customers of the maintenance process to determine if there are repetitive failures that need to be addressed. If so, record EVIDENCE of those failures to the right.)	

6.3.a and 6.3.c	5. (Verify throughout the audit that other related infrastructure requirements have been adequately addressed. These may include: a. Buildings b. Workspace c. Utilities d. Software needs e. Communication f. Internal transportation (i.e., fork lifts, etc.) (Note any exceptions to the right.)	
6.4	Work Environment (Verify throughout the audit that the appropriate work environment exists to achieve conformity to customer requirements. Examples may include lighting, temperature, noise, vibration, ergonomics, safety programs, etc.)	

CLAUSE 7	PRODUCT REALIZATION		
7.1	Planning of Product Realization		
	1. What is the planning process for new or changed products or manufacturing processes? Who is responsible for these activities? (Study any available documentation and interview auditees to understand the process.)		
	2. (Select \<X\> new or changed products or processes and verify the following:		
7.1.a	a. Were product requirements and quality objectives defined? May I see them?		
7.1.b	b. Were processes, documentation, and resources evaluated as appropriate to ensure that they were made suitable for the new product or process? (Look for evidence that any identified action items were completed.)		
7.1.c	c. Were required verification, validation, monitoring, inspection, and test activities clearly defined along with acceptance criteria? May I see them?		

7.1.d	d. Are records available to verify that processes and products met specified requirements?		
7.2	Customer Related Processes 1. How does <your organization> define and document customer requirements? (Study any documentation and interview auditees to understand how the process works.)		
7.2.1	2. Do <customer contracts, customer orders, product specifications, packaging standards, etc.> clearly and adequately define customer requirements including delivery and post-delivery requirements? (Select <X> such records and complete the matrix on the following page.)		
7.2.1.b and 7.2.1.c	3. How are regulatory and statutory requirements defined? How are any other requirement not necessarily stated by the customer, but required for the product's known and intended use, defined? Who is responsible for this?		

7.2.2	4. If <your organization> cannot meet the customers' requirements – including ship date – or if requirements on the order are different from those in the contract, how is that resolved with the customer? By whom? What records are maintained? (Pull <X> such records and verify compliance to planned arrangements.)
7.2.2	5. How are changes to customer requirements reviewed? By whom? What records are maintained? How are affected employees notified of the changes? (Pull <X> records and verify conformance. Ensure that any documentation was updated as a result of the change.)

CUSTOMER-RELATED PROCESS – AUDIT MATRIX

<Order #, project #, contract #, or customer PO #> audited	Were delivery requirements defined?	Was the product specification (or service standard) defined?	Is there evidence that requirements were reviewed?	Did the shipment or delivery meet delivery requirements?	Did the product or service meet specified requirements?	Comments

Effectiveness of 7.2.2	6. (Review the customer complaint file to look for any possible repetitive complaints due to unclear customer requirements or requirements agreed upon that <your organization> simply could not meet. Be sure to include delivery and service performance in this review as well as product nonconformities.)		
7.2.3	Customer Communication		
7.2.3.a	1. Please describe how the customer would communicate with <your organization> to obtain product information.		
7.2.3.b	2. What arrangements are in place for the customer to make inquiries, initiate a contract, place an order, or change an order? Are these arrangements clearly defined?		
7.2.3.c	3. How would a customer provide feedback or submit a complaint to <your organization>? Is this process clearly defined?		

	Design and Development	Project #	Project #	Project #
7.3	1. Describe the design and development process. (Study any documentation and interview auditees to understand how the process works.)			
7.3	2. (Select <X> recently closed projects and verify the following:	___	___	___
7.3.1	a. Is a project plan available for each project?			
7.3.1.c	b. Do plans identify specific activities along with the individual responsible for completing them?			
7.3.1.b	c. Do plans include the review, verification and validation activities that are appropriate to each stage of the design?			

Ref	Question
7.3.1	d. Who were the interfaces that were identified for each project? How were they kept abreast of the status of the design? (Pull records to verify conformance.)
7.3.1	e. Was the plan updated as necessary as the project evolved?
7.3.2.a and 7.3.2.b	f. Were customer and regulatory requirements clearly defined for each project along with the functional and performance requirements for the product? Were these requirements reviewed and approved? (Pull evidence.)
7.3.2.c	g. Were "lessons learned" from previous projects reviewed at the beginning of each project?
7.3.3.a	h. Is there evidence for each project that the design output <i.e.: prints, drawings, specifications, verification and validation results, etc.> met the customer and regulatory requirements specified in the question above?

7.3.3.c	i. Does design output include or reference acceptance criteria?
7.3.3.d	j. Do the output documents specify the characteristics of the product that are essential for its safe and proper use?
7.3.4	k. Are records available to show evidence of design review for each project at the required intervals? Were appropriate functions involved in each review? Were follow-up activities recorded?
7.3.5	l. Were verification requirements clearly defined and documented? (Pull verification records and verify that requirements were successfully completed or that follow-up activities were recorded.)
7.3.6	m. Were validation requirements clearly defined and documented? (Pull validation records and verify that requirements were successfully completed or follow-up activities were recorded.)

7.3.7	n. Have any of the projects had any changes? If so, verify that they were reviewed, verified, validated, and approved as appropriate. Was the effect of the change on other parts or the finished product evaluated? Do records include the results of the review as well as any necessary actions?	
Effectiveness of 7.3	3. What metrics are maintained to evaluate the effectiveness of the design and development process? <i.e.: Conformance to the schedule? Conformance to budget requirements? Verification and/or validation failures? Design failures in production? Etc.> (Evaluate these metrics for opportunities for improvements. Note opportunities to the right and as observations on the audit report.)	
Effectiveness of 7.3, 7.3.3.b	4. Interview the "customers" of the design and development process to ensure that the output is providing adequate information to operations, purchasing, maintenance, QA, etc.	

a. Are operations personnel getting adequate information to run the process?	
b. Are purchasing personnel getting adequate information on raw material specs, etc. in time to get acceptable materials from qualified suppliers?	
c. Are QA personnel getting adequate information in time to effectively test the new product?	
d. Are maintenance personnel getting adequate information to effectively maintain the equipment?	

7.4	**Purchasing** 1. How are suppliers of quality-related goods and services evaluated and approved? (Study any documentation and interview auditees to understand the system.)		
7.4.1	2. Are qualification requirements for new suppliers clearly defined and documented? May I see the requirements, please? (Pull \<X\> current supplier files at random and verify that records are available to show compliance to the requirements. If any suppliers have been approved in the last year, pull their files to verify compliance to the qualification requirements.)		
7.4.1	3. How are suppliers re-evaluated? (Pull records to verify compliance to established requirements. Where records show evidence of poor performance, follow through to ensure that corrective action has been initiated and that progress is being made.)		
7.4.1. 7.4.2	4. Pull \<X\> purchase orders at random and complete the matrix on the following page.		

Purchasing – 7.4.1 / 7.4.2

Purchase order number	Was supplier qualified per specified criteria?	Has supplier been re-evaluated per specified criteria?	Are all applicable requirements specified on the PO?	Was PO reviewed for adequacy before it was issued?	Comments

7.4.3	Verification of purchased product			
	1. Describe the incoming inspection process. (Study any documentation and interview auditees to understand the process.)			
	2. (Select <X> incoming materials at random and verify the requirements on the matrix following this section.)			
	3. Did all incoming materials meet specified requirements? If not, how were they controlled to ensure that they were not used until proper authorization was received?			
	4. If at-source inspection applies, how does <your organization> define acceptance criteria for incoming materials which are inspected or otherwise verified AT THE SUPPLIERS' FACILITY before it is shipped to you? (Pull records to verify compliance.)			

5.	(Review records of nonconformances in production. Approximately what percent is due to nonconforming incoming materials? What is the overall delivery performance of suppliers? Have repetitive late deliveries caused production downtime or resulted in any premium freight charges?) Is there anything that needs to be done to make the purchasing/receiving process more effective? (Discuss with production and receiving personnel. Record any specific opportunities for improvement as observations of the audit report.)

INCOMING INSPECTION – AUDIT MATRIX

Incoming product audited	Were test requirements clearly defined?	Were acceptable limits clearly defined?	Were required tests performed on previous 5 shipments?	Were test results within limits?	Was the individual responsible for release identified in the records?	Comments

Production and Service Provision		
Control of production and service provision		
NOTE: The auditing of control of production and service provision will be highly dependent upon the organization being audited. The following is a sample of questions, but these may need significant customization to apply to your organization.		
7.5		
7.5.1		
7.5.1 1. How is the process scheduled to ensure that required ship dates are met? How is this information communicated to operations personnel? (Look at production schedules and interview operations personnel to evaluate the effectiveness of this process.)		
7.5.1.a 2. What information is available to operations personnel that describes the characteristics of the product? <i.e.: Product specifications? Visual sample boards? Etc.> (Verify document control.)		

7.5.1.b and effectiveness of 7.5.1.b	3. What documentation is available to the operator for instruction on their activities? <i.e.: prints, drawings, work instructions, work packages, routers, travelers, etc.> (Question <X> operators at random to ensure that current revisions of documents are available where they are needed. Select <X> new employees, if possible, to ask about the effectiveness of this documentation. Is it too detailed? Not detailed enough? Obsolete? Wrong? Or very useful in learning the job?)	
7.5.1.c	4. (Verify throughout the audit that suitable equipment is used in production. Are there any repetitive problems associated with process equipment? Note any opportunities for improvement to the right. (Refer to section 6.3 for maintenance of that equipment.)	
7.5.1.d 7.5.1.e	5. What measuring and monitoring devices are used to ensure that customer requirements are met? May I see them, please? (Select <X> parameters at random for each area audited and verify the following:	

a. Are acceptance limits defined and documented? Are they available to the operator?		
b. (Pull records at random from the past several months. Do records show evidence that parameters are within specified limits? If not, was action taken as specified in the procedures? Record those records reviewed and results found to the right.)		
6. Describe the process for releasing and shipping product to ensure that only acceptable product is shipped to the correct customer.	7.5.1.f	
7. What post-delivery activities are conducted at <your organization>? (Compare records to planned arrangements to verify compliance.)	7.5.1.f	

7.5.1 Effectiveness	8. What objectives are monitored, if any, to verify the effectiveness of the production process? <i.e.: Productivity, scrap rates, rework rates, on-time delivery performance, etc.> May I see them please? (Verify that objectives are being achieved. If not, verify that appropriate action is being taken.)	
7.5.2	Verification of processes for production and service provision 1. Does <your organization> have any processes for which the resulting product cannot be verified by inspection and testing? How are the processes validated to demonstrate that planned results have been achieved?	
7.5.2	2. Does this validation include, as appropriate: a. Defined criteria for review and approval of the process? b. Approval of equipment and qualification of personnel?	

	c. Use of specific methods and procedures? d. Requirements for records? e. Revalidation requirements?			
7.5.3	Identification and traceability 1. How are incoming materials, in-process materials, and final products clearly identified? (Study any documentation and interview auditees to understand the process.)			
7.5.3	2. (Walk through storage and production areas to verify compliance to the procedures. Note any exceptions to the right.)			
7.5.3	3. What are the traceability requirements for <Your organization>? (Study procedures and interview auditees to understand the process.)			
7.5.3	4. (Pull records to verify conformance to any traceability requirements.)			

7.5.3 Effectiveness	5. Have mixed parts, mislabeled parts, shipping of wrong parts, etc. been a problem for <your organization>? (Discuss with auditees. Note any specific opportunities for improvement as observations in the audit report.)		
7.5.3	6. How is the inspection and test status of incoming materials, in-process materials and final products identified? (Study procedures and interview auditees to understand the process.)		
7.5.3	7. (Walk through the facility and verify conformance to procedures. Note any exceptions to the right.)		
7.5.4	Customer Property

1. What customer-supplied products does <your organization> receive, if any? How are these products inspected when they are received to ensure that they are fit for use? (Study procedures and interview auditees to understand the process.) | | |

7.5.4	2. (Pull receiving records to verify conformance to planned arrangements.)		
7.5.4	3. How are customer-supplied products handled, stored, protected and safeguarded to protect their fitness for use? (Walk through storage areas to look for evidence of conformance to procedures.)		
7.5.4	4. What process is in place to notify the customer of any problems associated with their materials? (Pull records to verify conformance.)		
7.5.5	Preservation of product 1. How are products handled and stored to protect their fitness for use? <i.e.: what specific handling and storage issues do you have at your facility? Electrostatic Discharge (ESD) concerns? Shelf lives on products or raw materials? Fork truck damage? Temperature and/or humidity-controlled storage areas? Double and triple stacking of cartons that crush the bottom carton? Broken bags? Etc.> (Study any documentation and interview auditees to understand the process.)		

7.5.5	2. (Pull records as required and walk through storage areas to verify conformance to procedures.)	
7.5.5	3. How does <your organization> ensure that product is packaged and labeled to meet any customer requirements? (Observe product being packaged. Ensure that correct procedures are being followed.)	

7.6	Control of Measuring and Monitoring Devices 1. Describe the calibration process at \<your organization\>. Does it include both process monitoring and product testing equipment? (Study any documentation and interview auditees to understand the process.)		
7.6	2. Are standards used to calibrate instruments certified against nationally recognized standards? If not, is the basis used for calibration clearly documented?		
7.6	3. (In each area responsible for calibration, select 3-5 instruments and verify the requirements on the matrix following this section.)		
7.6	4. Is any applicable software included in the calibration process?		

7.6	5. (Throughout the audit, verify that instruments and standards are handled and stored in a way that protects their fitness for use. Verify that they are safeguarded against adjustments that would invalidate calibration settings. Note any exceptions to the right.)	
7.6	6. (Throughout the audit, look for instruments found to be out of calibration when they were initially submitted for calibration. Verify that an assessment of previous results took place to confirm their accuracy and that any required action was taken relative to potentially nonconforming product.)	
7.6	7. (Throughout the audit, look for instruments that were repetitively found to be out of calibration. If this situation exists, has appropriate corrective action been initiated?)	

CONTROL OF MEASURING AND MONITORING DEVICES – AUDIT MATRIX

Instrument audited (include unique identification)	Calibration status current?	Any damage or deterioration noted?	Frequency of checks	Results within acceptable limits?	Is standard used to check this instrument traceable to a nationally recognized standard?	Comments

234 ◆ *ISO 9001:2000 Internal Audits Made Easy*

CLAUSE 8	MEASUREMENT, ANALYSIS AND IMPROVEMENT			
8.1	General requirements 1. Describe the processes used at <your organization> for monitoring, measurement, analysis and improvement needed to demonstrate product quality, conformance of the quality management system to the requirements of ISO 9001:2000, and ensure continual improvement of the effectiveness of the quality management system.			
8.1	2. What statistical techniques are used at <your organization>? What training or instruction is provided to ensure that techniques are used properly?			
8.2.1	Customer satisfaction How does <your organization> measure and monitor your customers' perception of your ability to meet their requirements? May I see it, please? (Verify that objectives are being achieved. Verify that appropriate action is being taken as indicated by the results.)			

8.2.2	Internal audit 1. How are internal audits planned and conducted? (Study procedures and interview auditees to understand the process.) May I see the internal audit schedule, please?			
8.2.2	2. (Select <X> audit reports at random and complete the Internal Audit matrix on the following page.)			
8.2.2/8.5.2	3. (Select <X> corrective actions that were initiated as a result of the internal audit process and complete the following Corrective Action matrix.)			
8.2.2 – Effectiveness	4. During the previous year, what specific improvements to the business have resulted from the internal audit process? Is there anything that needs to be done to improve the effectiveness of internal audits? (Discuss these issues with the auditees and record any specific opportunities for improvement as observations in the audit report.			

INTERNAL AUDIT – AUDIT MATRIX

Internal audit report audited	Was audit conducted on schedule?		Were auditors independent of the area audited?	Were auditors trained/qualified per the procedure?	Was management notified of audit results?	Comments

CORRECTIVE ACTION – AUDIT MATRIX

Corrective Action Request Number	Was the cause of the problem identified?	Was action taken to eliminate the cause?	Is there evidence that action taken was effective?	Were any associated documents updated as a result of action?	Was corrective action completed in a timely manner?	Comments

8.2.3	Monitoring and Measurement of Processes 1. (Verify throughout the audit that methods for measuring and monitoring of quality management system processes are effectively implemented. Where planned results are not achieved, verify that appropriate corrective action is being taken. Note any exceptions to the right.)		
8.2.4	Monitoring and Measurement of Product 1. What in-process inspection and testing is performed at <your organization>? (Study any documentation and interview auditees to understand the process.)		
8.2.4	2. (Select <X> in-process materials at random and verify the requirements in the matrix following this section.)		
8.2.4	3. Did all in-process materials meet specified requirements? If not, were they controlled and dispositioned per the Control of Nonconforming Product Procedure?		

8.2.4	4. What final product inspection and testing is performed at <your organization>? (Study any documentation and interview auditees to understand the process.)	
8.2.4	5. (Select <X> final products at random and verify requirements on the matrix following this section.)	
8.2.4	6. Did all final products meet customers' specified requirements? If nonconforming product was shipped, is the appropriate approval on file?	

IN-PROCESS INSPECTION AND TESTING – AUDIT MATRIX

In-Process product audited	Were test requirements clearly defined?	Were acceptable limits clearly defined?	Were required tests performed on <X> samples?	Were test results within limits?	Was the individual responsible for release identified in the records?	Comments

FINAL PRODUCT INSPECTION AND TESTING – AUDIT MATRIX

Final product audited	Were test requirements clearly defined?	Were acceptable limits clearly defined?	Were required tests performed on previous <X> shipments?	Were test results within limits?	Was the individual responsible for release identified in the records?	Comments

8.3	Control of nonconforming product
	1. How are nonconforming incoming materials, in-process materials, and final products controlled to prevent them from being further processed or shipped without the required approval? (Study procedures and interview auditees to understand the process.)
8.3	2. (Walk through production and storage areas and verify conformance to the documented procedure.)
8.3	3. Who has the authority to approve or to dispose of nonconforming materials? (Pull records for <X> nonconforming materials and verify that the disposition was made and documented by the authorized person(s).)
8.3	4. (Where rework was required for the above materials, verify that the materials were reinspected after the rework to verify that customer requirements were met.)

8.3	5. When nonconforming product is detected after shipment, what action is taken? (Pull records to verify conformance to the procedure.)		
8.3 Effectiveness	6. How are nonconformances tracked and monitored for opportunities to reduce them? (Pull corrective action records to verify that appropriate action is being taken.)		
8.4	Analysis of data 1. What specific data at \<your organization\> is collected and analyzed to demonstrate the effectiveness of the quality management system and to evaluate opportunities for continual improvement? May I see examples, please?		
8.4	2. (Verify that information is collected and analyzed for:) a. Customer satisfaction b. Conformance to product (or service) requirements		

	c. Characteristics and trends of processes and products (including opportunities for preventive actions) d. Supplier performance	
8.4	3. (Verify that appropriate action is taken based on the analysis of the data collected. Note any exceptions to the right.)	
8.5	Continual improvement 1. (Verify throughout the audit that <your organization> can demonstrate evidence of continual improvement through the review of the quality policy and objectives, analysis of data, corrective and preventive actions, and management review.)	

8.5.2 Corrective action 1. How are corrective actions initiated and processed to ensure that they are thoroughly addressed? Is corrective action initiated for nonconforming products or services and for customer complaints? (Study procedures and interview auditees to understand the process.)		
8.5.2 2. (Select <X> <Corrective Action Requests> at random and verify the requirements on the following page. Pull a representative sample of corrective actions for nonconformities, customer complaints, internal audits, etc.)		
8.5.2 Effectiveness 3. In the past year, what specific improvements to the business have resulted from the corrective action process? <i.e., reduced scrap? Less rework? Fewer customer complaints? More efficient processes? More streamlined processes? Etc.> Is there anything that needs to be done to make this process more effective? (Discuss these issues with the auditee. Note any opportunities for improvement as observations in the audit report.)		

CORRECTIVE ACTION – AUDIT MATRIX

Corrective Action Request Number	Was the cause of the problem identified?	Was action taken to eliminate the cause?	Is there evidence that action taken was effective?	Were any associated documents updated as a result of action?	Was corrective action completed in a timely manner?	Comments

8.5.3	Preventive action How is preventive action addressed at \<your organization\>? (Study procedures and interview auditees to understand the process.)	
8.5.3	(Pull \<X\> records of preventive action and verify conformance to the preventive action procedure.)	
8.5.3 Effectiveness	In the past year, what specific improvements to the business have resulted from the preventive action process? Is there anything that needs to be done to make this process more effective? (Discuss these issues with the auditee. Note any opportunities for improvement as observations in the audit report.)	

Appendix C

Audit Preparation Example

- Acme training procedure
- Acme Job Description
- Acme Training Checklist
- Sample audit checklist for Acme's training process

Issue Date: January 3, 2002   BP-18-01

Approved by: Ann W. Phillips (signature on File)   Revision 0

                                                                Page 1 of 2

Acme Business Procedure

Training

I.   Purpose:

The purpose of this procedure is to describe the system for ensuring that Acme employees are properly qualified and competent.

II.   Scope:

This procedure applies to all employees at Acme.

III. References

ISO 9001:2000, Section 6.2, Human Resources
ISO 14001:1996, Section 4.4.2, Training, Awareness and Competence
Acme Business Manual, Section 6.2
Training Checklists
Job Descriptions

IV.   Procedure

1.0.   New Employee Training

1.1.   The HR Manager maintains a Job Description and a Training Checklist for each position at Acme. The Job Descriptions identify specific qualification requirements; the Training Checklists define specific training needs. These documents can be found in the Forms Manual in the Administrative offices.

1.2.   When a new employee is hired, the HR Manager assigns a sponsor to the new employee who, along with the HR Manager, is responsible for ensuring that each item on the checklist is addressed. As an item is covered and the new employee can demonstrate the knowledge or skill to the sponsor, the sponsor initials that item on the checklist. When the checklist is completed, the applicable manager or supervisor reviews each item with the new employee to ensure understanding and to evaluate the effectiveness of training, then signs and dates the checklist along with the new employee.

1.3.   The HR Manager maintains completed checklists for each employee.

1.4. Approximately six months after the training has been completed, the HR Manager sends each new employee a questionnaire to further evaluate the effectiveness of the training and suggest opportunities to improve the training. The HR Manager reviews each evaluation and makes appropriate improvements to the training program.

1.5. Employees with at least six months' experience at their position as of December 31, 1999 are considered qualified based on their experience. The HR Manager has placed a Qualification Letter in the training file of each employee qualified on experience.

2.0. On-Going Training Needs

2.1. On-going training needs for the company are assessed annually during Management Review. Identified needs are forwarded to the HR Manager who is responsible for ensuring that identified training needs are met.

2.2. Individual training needs are assessed during annual performance reviews. The applicable department manager is responsible for ensuring that identified training is provided.

2.3. The ESHA department is responsible for scheduling and performing annual training required be safety and environmental regulations.

2.4. The HR Manager maintains records of on-going training in the employee's training file.

V. Records:

The HR Manager maintains training records for each employee. These records are kept in the Administration area during the employment of the individual plus two years. Training records are filed alphabetically by the employee's last name.

VI. Nature of Revisions in the Latest Issue

None – New issue

Job Description

Position: Quality Assurance Lab Technician II

Reports To: Quality Assurance Supervisor

Minimum Qualifications: High school diploma, 3 years experience in chemical plant laboratory testing or equivalent

Key Responsibilities:

Safely test raw materials, in-process materials, and final product in accordance with documented test methods referenced below to ensure that materials and products meet specified requirements.

- Raw material testing
  - pH (LM-01)
  - Viscosity (LM-02)
  - Hydroxyl numbers (LM-03)
  - Infrared spectroscopy (LM-04)
  - UV analysis (LM-05)
  - Liquid chromatography (LM-06)
  - Gas Chromatography (LM-07)

- In-process and final product testing
  - Intrinsic viscosity (LM-08)
  - Melt point (LM-09)
  - Color (LM-10)
  - Visual (LM-11)

- Instrument maintenance and calibration (See MP-06, Control of Measuring and Monitoring Devices, for a list of instruments in the maintenance and calibration process along with specific responsibilities and a reference to the appropriate calibration methods.)

- Complying with safety rules and regulations in the lab
  - Proper use of ventilation hoods (LM-12)
  - Proper labeling of samples and reagents (MP-03, Identification of Products and Materials)
  - Proper use of PPE (safety glasses, gloves, and hearing protection where required)

- Identify any hazards noted throughout the facility, and notify your supervisor about these hazards. Immediately correct those that you have the ability to correct.

- Properly label of laboratory samples and chemicals.

- Properly label laboratory samples and chemicals.

- Properly label and handle laboratory wastes in accordance with LM-13.

- Do not pour chemicals down the sink drain.

- Follow environmental procedures and relevant work instructions (as identified by the supervisor).

- Immediately notify the supervisor of any chemical spill.

- Minimize use and waste of chemicals.

- Record maintenance (See MP-02, Control of Records, for a list of those records to be maintained, by whom, and where.)

Training Checklist

Position: Quality Assurance Lab Technician

Name: Bob Smith

Job Description Number: QA-05

Date of Hire: January 4, 2001

Sponsor: Mary Jones

Trained
By: Date:

_____ _____ 1. Acme Company Quality Policy Statement

_____ _____ 2. Roles and responsibilities in achieving the policy (QA-05)

_____ _____ 3. QA Laboratory quality, environmental and OH&S objectives, and the roles and responsibilities of the QA Lab Technician in achieving those objectives.

_____ _____ 4. Lotus Notes based document management system. (BP-01)

_____ _____ 5. Hazard assessment and risk analysis for laboratory function/Hazard recognition process. (Training Package #3)

_____ _____ 6. HazCom training (Training Package #6)

_____ _____ 7. Hearing conservation training (Training Package #2)

_____ _____ 8. Required personal protective equipment (safety glasses, gloves, and hearing protection where required)

_____ _____ 9. Impact of laboratory wastes on the environment. Proper waste disposal methods. (LM-13) (Significant environmental aspect)

_____ _____ 10. Use of ventilation hoods (LM-12)

_____ _____ 11. Proper labeling of samples and reagents (MP-03)

 12. Inspection and test methods including maintenance and calibration of instruments:

_____ _____   a. pH (LM-01)

_____ _____   b. Viscosity (LM-02)

_____ _____   c. Hydroxyl number (LM-03)

_____ _____   d. Infrared spectroscopy (LM-04)

_____ _____   e. UV analysis (LM-05)

_____ _____   f. Liquid chromatography (LM-06)

_____ _____   g. Gas chromatography (LM-07)

_____ _____   h. Intrinsic viscosity (LM-08)

_____ _____   i. Melt point (LM-09)

_____ _____   j. Color (LM-10)

_____ _____   k. Visual inspection (LM-11)

_____ _____ 12. Records to be maintained by the QA Laboratory Technician (MP-02)

Other important information:

- Never use an obsolete revision of a laboratory method, management procedure, training package, or form. If in doubt, the current revision status of a document is available through the plant documentation system on Lotus Notes.

- Always check the calibration status label of calibrated equipment and never use an instrument that is out of calibration.

- If a document that you are using needs revision, make the required changes in red ink, sign and date the changes, and turn it into your supervisor. If it isn't right, change it. You are the most accurate input for changing documents.

I have been trained on each of the items listed above and am comfortable that I can safely perform the tasks specified on my Job Description.

_____   _____
Employee's Signature   Date

_____   _____   _____   _____
Sponsor's Signature   Date   QA Supervisor's Signature   Date

Checklist – Section 6.2
Awareness, Competence and Training
Acme Manufacturing

REFERENCE	QUESTIONS	EVIDENCE	CAR#
6.2	Human Resources 1. How are competency requirements and training needs identified for new and current employees? Who is responsible for identifying these needs? How are the needs documented? How is training evaluated for effectiveness? (Study any documentation and interview auditees to understand the process.)		
6.2.2.a 6.2.2.b 6.2.2.c 6.2.2.d 6.2.2.e	2. (Pull training records for <X> new employees – or employees new to their position – who have been trained in the previous year and complete the matrix on the following page. Be sure to include any applicable management, technical, and administrative personnel who affect product quality as well as operators, lab technicians, and maintenance personnel.)		

NEW EMPLOYEE TRAINING – AUDIT MATRIX

New employee	Is there a current Job Description and Training Checklist for this position?	Do the Job Desc and Training Checklist adequately define competency requirements for this position?	Was the training checklist thoroughly completed?	Did the checklist identify appropriate documentation where applicable?	Did training include knowledge of company objectives and the employee's impact on them?	Did the new employee complete a New Employee Training Evaluation Form?

Verification of input	3. How are sponsors selected? What instruction, if any, are they given to ensure that training is effective?		
BP-18-01, Section	4. (Pull management review meeting minutes and verify that plant-wide training needs have been assessed during the previous year. Pull records to verify that identified training needs have been planned for or provided.)		
BP-18-01, Section	5. (Pull assessed training needs for five experienced employees at random. Pull records to verify that identified training needs have been planned for or provided.)		
6.2.2.c	6. How are New Employee Training Forms evaluated to identify opportunities to improve the training process? (Review the forms for any trends or significant comments that may indicate an opportunity for improvement. Verify that indicated action has indeed been taken.)		

7. (Interview new employees.)
 	
  a. Were you trained by the procedures or instructions in your department?
 	
  b. If so, were they helpful to you?
 	
  c. If not, why not? <Were they too short? Too long? Nonexistent? Incorrect? Obsolete? >
 	
  d. What have you learned since you have been at this organization that you wish had been included in the training process?
 	
  e. How would you rate our training process on a scale of 1-10? <If given a rating of 7 or lower> What suggestions could you give to improve the training process?
 	
Identify any opportunities to improve the training process to the right. List as observations in the audit report.	

Appendix D

Forms and Templates to Report Audit Results and Track Corrective Actions

- Audit Schedule Matrix
- Audit Summary Report
- Corrective Action Request (CAR)
- Corrective Action Request Log
- Audit Action Item List

AUDIT SCHEDULE MATRIX

ISO 9001 2000 Clause	Management	QA	Laboratory	Production	Purchasing	Warehouse Shipping	Engineering	Sales & Marketing	Order Entry	Human Resources	Maintenance
Clause 4.2.3*	E	X	O	E	O	E	O	E	O	E	O
Clause 5 Clause 6.1	X	X	E	O	E	O	E	O	E	O	E
Clause 6.2	A	A	A	A	A	A	A	A	A	X	A
Clauses 6.3 & 6.4			X	X	O	X	E	O	E	O	X
Clauses 7.1 & 7.5		X		X		X	X				
Clause 7.2			O	E	O			X	X		
Clause 7.3			O	E	O		X				E
Clause 7.4			X	X	X	E					O
Clause 7.6			X	X							X
Clauses 8.1, 8.2.1, 8.2.2, 8.4, & 8.5	A	X	A	A	A	A	A	X	A	A	A
Clauses 8.2.4 & 8.3		X	X	X							

- Clauses 4.1, 4.2.1, 4.2.2, 4.2.4, and 8.2.3 are audited in conjunction with every audit.

- X = this department plays a key role in the process(es) being audited and should be audited every year

  E, O = these departments play a more peripheral role in process(es) being audited and can be audited every other year (E = even-numbered years; O = odd-numbered years)

  A = the audit should go into those departments indicated by the records.

Audit Summary Report

To:

An audit of the _____ process within the quality management system was performed on _____. Departments involved in the audit included:

_____

_____

The auditors included:

_____   _____

A summary of the findings is given below:

CAR: Brief description

_____   _____

_____   _____

_____   _____

_____   _____

Observations are recorded on the attached Audit Action Item List

Opportunities for improvement included:

_____

_____

_____

_____

Examples of continual improvement noted since the last audit included:

_____

_____

_____

_____

Thank you very much for your cooperation in making this audit a success. Please remember that Corrective Action Requests are due back to me with proposed action items and estimated completion dates by_____.

Thank you,

Corrective Action Request

Reason

CAR #: _____

____ Internal Audit

Date: _____

____ External Audit

Initiator: _____

____ Customer Complaint

____ Product Nonconformity

____ Other: _____

_____

Describe the problem:

Probable cause:

Management Representative Approval:

Action Plan:

Estimated completion date: _____   Actual Completion date:

_____

Verification of effectiveness (record of EVIDENCE that corrective action has been effective or reference a new CAR #)

Have associated documents been updated as necessary?   _____ yes   _____ no

Signed: _____   Date: _____

CORRECTIVE ACTION LOG

CAR #	Date Initiated	Assigned To	Estimated Completion Date	Actual Completion Date	Planned Verification Date	Actual Verification Date

AUDIT ACTION ITEM LIST

Action Item	Audit Date	Assigned To:	Action Taken	Date Completed	Verification Date

About the Author

ANN PHILLIPS is the Executive Vice President of Management Systems with Omni Tech International, Ltd. Since August 1991, she has assisted numerous companies, ranging from small distributors to worldwide corporations, in their pursuit of ISO 9001/QS-9000 registration. Over one hundred fifty clients have achieved registration. A sampling of the industries/organizations with whom she has worked includes:

Manufacturing:
- Chemical
- Automotive
- Aerospace
- Pulp and Paper
- Container Corporations
- Medical Products

Services:
- Shipyards
- Engineering and Consulting Firms
- Medical and Health Services
- The Federal Aviation Administration
- Distributors
- Transportation

Her emphasis is on implementing practical and effective management systems in a way that achieves measurable improvements in the business. Ms. Phillips is certified by the Registrar Accreditation Board as a Quality Systems Auditor.

Prior to August 1991, Ms. Phillips worked with 3M and Dupont as a Quality Engineer, Quality Manager, and Occupational Health and Safety Supervisor. During that time, she audited quality management systems at numerous supplier organizations; lead the ISO 9001 implementation process at a chemical facility; and coordinated safety and health systems with the ISO 9001 management system.

In addition to on-site consulting and training, Ms. Phillips has instructed regularly for the University of Houston at Clear Lake, the Center for Quality at Eastern Michigan University, Collin County Community College, the American Society for Quality (ASQ), and the American Production and Inventory Control Society (APICS).

Ms. Phillips graduated summa cum laude from Furman University with a BS degree in Chemistry. She is a popular speaker at management system conferences throughout the country.

Internal Audit Seminars

Ms. Phillips presents seminars on effective internal audit techniques throughout the year. A sampling of comments following those classes include:

"Outstanding! The instructor certainly knows her stuff—brilliant in every detail, personable, outgoing, and extremely bright!"
— Rance Lucas, M.W. Kellogg Co.

"I have taken more quality-related courses than I can remember—this course has been the most remarkable both in presentation and content. Ann's the best I've ever encountered!"
— Carolyn Condon, Consultant

"Ann Phillips is truly the best! Everything fits now. I understand."
— Louis Daigle, Montell USA

"This has, by far, been the most informative and fun class I have ever had the opportunity to attend, thanks to Ann Phillips."
— Wanda Brazeal, Thermo-Temp

"This is one of the best seminars I've ever attended. Ann Phillips is very knowledgeable about her subject and an outstanding instructor."
— Anita Fogtman, Loral Space Systems

"Phenomenal! Ann Phillips has renamed this course. . . ISO Auditing for dummies disguised as experts"
— Jackie Johnson, Bayer Corporation

For a schedule of seminars provided by Ann Phillips and others at Omni Tech International, please reference our website at *www.omnitechintl.com*.